KU-176-441

Fremdsprachentexte

H. G. Wells
The Invisible Man

Herausgegeben von
Klaus Werner

Philipp Reclam jun. Stuttgart

Universal-Bibliothek Nr. 9013
Alle Rechte vorbehalten
© für diese Ausgabe 1994 Philipp Reclam jun. GmbH & Co., Stuttgart
Copyright für den Text The Literary Executors of the Estate of
H. G. Wells. Abdruck mit Genehmigung von A. P. Watt Ltd., London
Gesamtherstellung: Reclam, Ditzingen. Printed in Germany 1994
RECLAM und UNIVERSAL-BIBLIOTHEK sind eingetragene
Warenzeichen der Philipp Reclam jun. GmbH & Co., Stuttgart
ISBN 3-15-009013-X

The Invisible Man

Chapter I

The Strange Man's Arrival

The stranger came early in February one wintry day,
through a biting wind and a driving snow, the last snow-
fall of the year, over the down, walking as it seemed from
Bramblehurst railway station and carrying a little black
portmanteau in his thickly gloved hand. He was
wrapped up from head to foot, and the brim of his soft
felt hat hid every inch of his face but the shiny tip of his
nose; the snow had piled itself against his shoulders and
chest, and added a white crest to the burden he carried.
He staggered into the Coach and Horses, more dead
than alive as it seemed, and flung his portmanteau down.
"A fire," he cried, "in the name of human charity! A
room and a fire!" He stamped and shook the snow from

---

6 **down:** allg.: baumloser Höhenzug; speziell: kahle, hügelige Landschaft im Süden Englands; gemeint sind hier die *South Downs* in Sussex.
8 **portmanteau** (Fr., pl. *portmanteaux*): Handkoffer.
9 **brim:** Rand, Krempe.
10 **felt:** Filz.
12 **crest:** (Feder-)Schopf; hier (fig.): Haube.
13 **the Coach and Horses:** Name eines Gasthofs.
15 **charity:** Barmherzigkeit.

off himself in the bar, and followed Mrs. Hall into her
guest parlour to strike his bargain. And with that much
introduction, that and a ready acquiescence to terms and
a couple of sovereigns flung upon the table, he took up
5 his quarters in the inn.

Mrs. Hall lit the fire and left him there while she went to
prepare him a meal with her own hands. A guest to stop
at Iping in the winter-time was an unheard-of piece of
luck, let alone a guest who was no "haggler," and she was
10 resolved to show herself worthy of her good fortune. As
soon as the bacon was well under way, and Millie, her
lymphatic aid, had been brisked up a bit by a few deftly
chosen expressions of contempt, she carried the cloth,
plates, and glasses into the parlour and began to lay
15 them with the utmost *éclat*. Although the fire was burning up briskly, she was surprised to see that her visitor
still wore his hat and coat, standing with his back to her
and staring out of the window at the falling snow in the
yard. His gloved hands were clasped behind him, and he
20 seemed to be lost in thought. She noticed that the melted

2 **guest parlour:** Gastzimmer.
  to strike a bargain: eine Einigung treffen, verhandeln.
2 f. **with that much introduction:** etwa: ohne ein weiteres Wort zu ver-
  lieren.
3 **acquiescence:** Einwilligung, Zustimmung.
4 **sovereign:** ehemals englische Goldmünze im Wert von 20 Shilling.
4 f. **to take up one's quarters** (pl.): Quartier beziehen.
9 **let alone:** ganz zu schweigen von.
  haggler: Feilscher (von *to haggle* ›feilschen‹).
11 **to be under way:** im Gange sein; hier: gerade gebraten werden.
12 **lymphatic:** träge, phlegmatisch.
  to brisk s.o. up: jdn. aufmuntern.
  deftly (adv.): geschickt.
15 **éclat** (Fr.): hier: Aufwand.
16 **briskly** (adv.): lebhaft, munter.

snow that still sprinkled his shoulders dripped upon her
carpet. "Can I take your hat and coat, sir," she said, "and
give them a good dry in the kitchen?"
"No," he said without turning.

5 She was not sure she had heard him, and was about to re-
peat her question.
He turned his head and looked at her over his shoulder.
"I prefer to keep them on," he said with emphasis, and
she noticed that he wore big blue spectacles with side-
10 lights and had a bushy side-whisker over his coat-collar
that completely hid his face.
"Very well, sir," she said. "*As* you like. In a bit the room
will be warmer."
He made no answer and had turned his face away from
15 her again; and Mrs. Hall, feeling that her conversational
advances were ill-timed, laid the rest of the table things
in a quick staccato and whisked out of the room. When
she returned he was still standing there like a man of
stone, his back hunched, his collar turned up, his drip-
20 ping hat-brim turned down, hiding his face and ears
completely. She put down the eggs and bacon with considerable emphasis, and called rather than said to him,
"Your lunch is served, sir."

1 **to sprinkle:** besprengen, (auf etwas) rieseln.
8 **emphasis:** Nachdruck.
9f. **side-lights:** Seitenteile einer Brille, die die Augen vor seitlich ein-
fallendem Licht schützen sollen.
10 **side-whisker** (auch: *whiskers*): Backenbart.
15f. **conversational advances:** Versuche, ein Gespräch in Gang zu bringen.
16 **to be ill-timed:** zeitlich schlecht gewählt sein.
17 **in a quick staccato:** mit raschen, abrupten Bewegungen.
   to whisk: huschen, sausen.
19 **hunched:** gebeugt, gekrümmt.

"Thank you," he said at the same time, and did not stir until she was closing the door. Then he swung round and approached the table.

As she went behind the bar to the kitchen she heard a
5 sound repeated at regular intervals. Chirk, chirk, chirk, it went, the sound of a spoon being rapidly whisked round a basin. "That girl!" she said. "There! I clean forgot it. It's her being so long!" And while she herself finished mixing the mustard, she gave Millie a few verbal
10 stabs for her excessive slowness. She had cooked the ham and eggs, laid the table, and done everything, while Millie (help indeed!) had only succeeded in delaying the mustard. And him a new guest and wanting to stay! Then she filled the mustard pot, and, putting it with a
15 certain stateliness upon a gold and black tea-tray, carried it into the parlour.

She rapped and entered promptly. As she did so her visitor moved quickly, so that she got but a glimpse of a white object disappearing behind the table. It would
20 seem he was picking something from the floor. She rapped down the mustard pot on the table, and then she noticed the overcoat and hat had been taken off and put over a chair in front of the fire. A pair of wet boots threatened rust to her steel fender. She went to these

---

6 **to whisk:** rasch bewegen, (mit einem Schneebesen) rühren, schlagen.
7 **clean** (adv.): ‚glatt', einfach.
8 **It's her being so long:** Das kommt von ihrer Langsamkeit.
9 **mustard:** Senf.
9f. **verbal stabs:** bissige Bemerkungen (*stab:* Hieb, Stich).
10 **excessive:** übertrieben.
15 **stateliness:** Würde.
17 **to rap:** klopfen.
21 **to rap down:** geräuschvoll hinstellen.
24 **steel fender:** Kamingitter.

things resolutely. "I suppose I may have them to dry now," she said in a voice that brooked no denial.

"Leave the hat," said her visitor in a muffled voice, and turning she saw he had raised his head and was sitting looking at her.

For a moment she stood gaping at him, too surprised to speak.

He held a white cloth – it was a serviette he had brought with him – over the lower part of his face, so that his mouth and jaws were completely hidden, and that was the reason of his muffled voice. But it was not that which startled Mrs. Hall. It was the fact that all his forehead above his blue glasses was covered by a white bandage, and that another covered his ears, leaving not a scrap of his face exposed excepting only his pink, peaked nose. It was bright pink, and shiny just as it had been at first. He wore a dark-brown velvet jacket with a high black linen-lined collar turned up about his neck. The thick black hair, escaping as it could below and between the cross bandages, projected in curious tails and horns, giving him the strangest appearance conceivable. This muffled and bandaged head was so unlike what she hat antici-pated, that for a moment she was rigid.

---

2 **to brook** (auch: *to take*) **no denial:** keinen Widerspruch dulden.
3 **muffled:** gedämpft, dumpf.
6 **to gape at s.o.:** jdn. anstarren.
10 **jaws:** Kinnbacken.
14 **scrap:** Stück(chen).
15 **to expose:** sichtbar machen.
   peaked nose: spitze Nase.
17 f. **linen-lined:** leinengefüttert.
20 **to project:** hervorlugen.
21 **conceivable:** denkbar.
22 f. **to anticipate:** erwarten.
23 **rigid:** erstarrt, starr.

He did not remove the serviette, but remained holding
it, as she saw now, with a brown gloved hand, and regarding her with his inscrutable blue glasses. "Leave the
hat," he said, speaking very distinctly through the white
5 cloth.
Her nerves began to recover from the shock they had received. She placed the hat on the chair again by the fire.
"I didn't know, sir," she began, "that –" and she stopped
embarrassed.
10 "Thank you," he said drily, glancing from her to the door
and then at her again.
"I'll have them nicely dried, sir, at once," she said, and
carried his clothes out of the room. She glanced at his
white-swathed head and blue goggles again as she was
15 going out of the door; but his napkin was still in front of
his face. She shivered a little as she closed the door behind her, and her face was eloquent of her surprise and
perplexity. "I *never*," she whispered. "There!" She went
quite softly to the kitchen, and was too preoccupied to
20 ask Millie what she was messing about with *now*, when
she got there.
The visitor sat and listened to her retreating feet. He
glanced inquiringly at the window before he removed

---

3 **inscrutable:** unergründlich.
14 **white-swathed:** weißverhüllt (*swathed:* verhüllt).
   goggles (pl.): Schutzbrille; hier auch: getönte Brille.
16 **to shiver:** zittern, schaudern.
17 **to be eloquent of s.th.:** etwas beredt ausdrücken (Gesicht).
18 **perplexity:** Verwirrung, Bestürzung.
   I never: *I never saw something like that.*
   there!: so etwas!
19 **preoccupied:** gedankenverloren, mit seinen, ihren Gedanken beschäftigt.
20 **to mess about with s.th.:** mit etwas herumwerkeln.
23 **inquiringly** (adv.): forschend.

his serviette and resumed his meal. He took a mouthful,
glanced suspiciously at the window, took another
mouthful, then rose and, taking the serviette in his hand,
walked across the room and pulled the blind down to the
top of the white muslin that obscured the lower panes.
This left the room in twilight. This done, he returned
with an easier air to the table and his meal.

"The poor soul's had an accident or an operation or
something," said Mrs. Hall. "What a turn them bandages
did give me, to be sure!"

She put on some more coal, unfolded the clothes-horse,
and extended the traveller's coat upon this. "And they
goggles! Why, he looked more like a divin' helmet than
a human man!" She hung his muffler on a corner of the
horse. "And holding that handkercher over his mouth
all the time. Talkin' through it! … Perhaps his mouth
was hurt too – maybe."

She turned round, as one who suddenly remembers.
"Bless my soul alive!" she said, going off at a tangent;
"ain't you done them taters *yet*, Millie?"

---

4 **blind:** *window-blind:* Rouleau.
5 **muslin:** Musselin, dünner weicher Baumwollstoff.
7 **with an easier air:** mit erleichterter Miene (*air:* Aussehen, Anschein, Miene).
9f. **What a turn them bandages did give me** (dial.): *What a turn those bandages did give me:* Wie hat mich sein Verband erschreckt.
11 **clothes-horse:** Wäscheständer.
12f. **they goggles** (dial.): *those goggles.*
13 **divin' helmet:** *diving-helmet:* Taucherhelm.
14 **muffler:** Halstuch.
15 **handkercher** (dial.): *handkerchief:* Tuch.
19 **to go off at a tangent:** (fig.) sich plötzlich einer anderen Sache zuwenden, plötzlich vom Thema abschweifen.
20 **ain't you** (dial.): *haven't you.*
   them taters (dial.): *those potatoes.*

When Mrs. Hall went to clear away the stranger's lunch,
her idea that his mouth must also have been cut or disfigured in the accident she supposed him to have suffered, was confirmed, for he was smoking a pipe, and all
5 the time that she was in the room he never loosened the
silk muffler he had wrapped round the lower part of his
face to put the mouthpiece to his lips. Yet it was not for-
getfulness, for she saw he glanced at it as it smouldered
out. He sat in the corner with his back to the window-
10 blind and spoke now, having eaten and drunk and being
comfortably warmed through, with less aggressive brevity than before. The reflection of the fire lent a kind of
red animation to his big spectacles they had lacked
hitherto.
15 "I have some luggage," he said, "at Bramblehurst station," and he asked her how he could have it sent. He
bowed his bandaged head quite politely in acknowledgment of her explanation. "To-morrow!" he said. "There
is no speedier delivery?" and seemed quite disappointed
20 when she answered, "No." Was she quite sure? No man
with a trap who would go over?
Mrs. Hall, nothing loath, answered his questions and developed a conversation. "It's a steep road by the down,
sir," she said in answer to the question about a trap; and
25 then, snatching at an opening, said, "It was there a car-

2f. **disfigured:** entstellt.
8f. **to smoulder out:** verglimmen, langsam ausgehen.
11f. **brevity:** Kürze.
13 **animation:** Lebhaftigkeit.
14 **hitherto** (adv.): bisher.
17f. **in acknowledgment of s.th.:** zum Dank für etwas.
21 **trap:** zweirädriger Pferdewagen.
22 **nothing loath** (adv.): bereitwillig.
25 **opening:** Anknüpfungspunkt.

riage was upsettled, a year ago and more. A gentleman
killed, besides his coachman. Accidents, sir, happen in a
moment, don't they?"
But the visitor was not to be drawn so easily. "They do,"
he said through his muffler, eyeing her quietly through
his impenetrable glasses.
"But they take long enough to get well, sir, don't they?
… There was my sister's son, Tom, jest cut his arm with
a scythe, tumbled on it in the 'ayfield, and, bless me! he
was three months tied up, sir. You'd hardly believe it. It's
regular given me a dread of a scythe, sir."
"I can quite understand that," said the visitor.
"He was afraid, one time, that he'd have to have an
opration – he was that bad, sir."
The visitor laughed abruptly, a bark of a laugh that
he seemed to bite and kill in his mouth. "*Was* he?" he
said.
"He was, sir. And no laughing matter to them as had the
doing for him, as I had – my sister being took up with her

---

1 **to upsettle:** umstürzen.
4 **to be drawn:** sich provozieren, aus der Reserve locken, die Würmer
aus der Nase ziehen lassen.
6 **impenetrable:** undurchdringlich.
8 **jest** (dial.): *just.*
9 **scythe:** Sense.
   'ayfield (dial.): *hayfield.* Der Wegfall des h (»aitch-dropping«) ist
   typisch für den Londoner (Cockney) und südwestenglischen Dialekt.
10 **tied up:** bandagiert.
10f. **It's regular given me a dread of a scythe:** Seitdem bekomme ich einen Schreck, wenn ich eine Sense sehe.
14 **opration** (dial.): *operation.*
18f. **no laughing matter to them as had the doing for him** (dial.): nichts
   zu lachen für die, die ihn pflegen mußten.
19 **took up** (dial.): *taken up:* beschäftigt.

little ones so much. There was bandages to do, sir, and
bandages to undo. So that if I may make so bold as to say
it, sir —"

"Will you get me some matches?" said the visitor, quite
5 abruptly. "My pipe is out."

Mrs. Hall was pulled up suddenly. It was certainly rude
of him, after telling him all she had done. She gasped at
him for a moment, and remembered the two sovereigns.
She went for the matches.

10 "Thanks," he said concisely, as she put them down, and
turned his shoulder upon her and stared out of the window again. It was altogether too discouraging. Evidently
he was sensitive on the topic of operations and bandages. She did not "make so bold as to say," however,
15 after all. But his snubbing way had irritated her, and
Millie had a hot time of it that afternoon.

The visitor remained in the parlour until four o'clock,
without giving the ghost of an excuse for an intrusion.
For the most part he was quite still during that time; it
20 would seem he sat in the growing darkness smoking in
the firelight, perhaps dozing.

---

1 **there was:** *there were.*
2 **to make so bold as to do s.th.:** sich die Freiheit nehmen, etwas zu tun.
6 **to pull s.o. up:** jdn. anhalten, zum Schweigen bringen.
10 **concisely** (adv.): knapp.
12 **discouraging:** entmutigend.
13 **sensitive:** empfindlich.
   topic: (Gesprächs-)Thema.
15 **his snubbing way:** seine abweisende Art (*to snub s.o.:* jdn. brüskieren,
   vor den Kopf stoßen).
16 **Millie had a hot time of it:** Millie mußte es ausbaden.
18 **ghost** (fig.): Schatten, Andeutung, Spur.
   intrusion: Betreten, Hineingehen.
21 **to doze:** dösen, (halb) schlummern.

Once or twice a curious listener might have heard him at the coals, and for the space of five minutes he was audible pacing the room. He seemed to be talking to himself. Then the armchair creaked as he sat down again.

Chapter II

Mr. Teddy Henfrey's First Impressions

At four o'clock, when it was fairly dark and Mrs. Hall was screwing up her courage to go in and ask her visitor if he would take some tea, Teddy Henfrey, the clock-jobber, came into the bar. "My sakes! Mrs. Hall," said he, "but this is terrible weather for thin boots!" The snow outside was falling faster.

Mrs. Hall agreed with him, and then noticed he had his bag and hit upon a brilliant idea. "Now you're here, Mr. Teddy," said she, "I'd be glad if you'd give th' old clock in the parlour a bit of a look. "Tis going, and it strikes well and hearty; but the hour-hand won't do nuthin' but point at six."

2 **space:** Zeitraum.
2f. **audible:** hörbar.
3 **to pace the room:** im Zimmer auf und ab, hin und her gehen.
4 **to creak:** knarren.
8 **to screw up one's courage:** seinen, ihren Mut zusammennehmen.
9f. **clock-jobber:** Uhrmacher.
10 **my sakes!:** bei Gott!
14 **to hit upon an idea:** auf eine Idee kommen.
17 **nuthin'** (dial.): *nothing*.

And leading the way, she went across to the parlour door
and rapped and entered.

Her visitor, she saw as she opened the door, was seated
in the armchair before the fire, dozing it would seem,
with his bandaged head drooping on one side. The only
light in the room was the red glow from the fire – which
lit his eyes like adverse railway signals, but left his downcast face in darkness – and the scanty vestiges of the day
that came in through the open door. Everything was
ruddy, shadowy, and indistinct to her, the more so since
she had just been lighting the bar lamp, and her eyes
were dazzled. But for a second it seemed to her that the
man she looked at had an enormous mouth wide open, –
a vast and incredible mouth that swallowed the whole of
the lower portion of his face. It was the sensation of a
moment: the white-bound head, the monstrous goggle
eyes, and this huge yawn below it. Then he stirred,
started up in his chair, put up his hand. She opened the
door wide, so that the room was lighter, and she saw him
more clearly, with the muffler held to his face just as she
had seen him hold the serviette before. The shadows,
she fancied, had tricked her.

"Would you mind, sir, this man a-coming to look at the

---

 5 **to droop:** hängen, (sich) neigen.
 7 **adverse:** hier: auf Halt gestellt.
 7f. **downcast:** nach unten geneigt.
 8 **scanty:** spärlich, schwach.
   vestige: (fig.) Spur.
10 **ruddy:** rot, rötlich.
12 **to dazzle:** blenden.
16f. **goggle eyes:** Glupsch-, Glotzaugen (*to goggle:* glotzen).
17 **yawn:** gähnende Leere.
23 **a-coming** (dial.): *coming.*

clock, sir?" she said, recovering from her momentary shock.

"Look at the clock?" he said, staring round in a drowsy manner and speaking over his hand, and then, getting
5 more fully awake, "certainly."

Mrs. Hall went away to get a lamp, and he rose and stretched himself. Then came the light, and Mr. Teddy Henfrey, entering, was confronted by this bandaged person. He was, he says, "taken aback."
10 "Good-afternoon," said the stranger, regarding him, as Mr. Henfrey says with a vivid sense of the dark spectacles, "like a lobster."

"I hope," said Mr. Henfrey, "that it's no intrusion."

"None whatever," said the stranger. "Though I under-
15 stand," he said, turning to Mrs. Hall, "that this room is really to be mine for my own private use."

"I thought, sir," said Mrs. Hall, "you'd prefer the clock –" She was going to say "mended."

"Certainly," said the stranger, "certainly – but, as a rule,
20 I like to be alone and undisturbed.

But I'm really glad to have the clock seen to," he said, seeing a certain hesitation in Mr. Henfrey's manner. "Very glad." Mr. Henfrey had intended to apologise and withdraw, but this anticipation reassured him. The
25 stranger stood round with his back to the fireplace and

---

3 **drowsy:** verschlafen.
9 **taken aback:** verblüfft.
11 **vivid:** (fig.) lebendig, lebhaft.
12 **lobster:** Hummer.
13 **intrusion:** Eindringen, Stören.
21 **to see to s.th.:** nach etwas sehen, sich um etwas kümmern.
24 **anticipation:** Zuvorkommen.
    to reassure: beruhigen.

put his hands behind his back. "And presently," he
said, "when the clock-mending is over, I think I should
like to have some tea. But not till the clock-mending is
over."

5 Mrs. Hall was about to leave the room, – she made no
conversational advances this time, because she did not
want to be snubbed in front of Mr. Henfrey, – when her
visitor asked her if she had made any arrangements
about his boxes at Bramblehurst. She told him she had

10 mentioned the matter to the postman, and that the carrier could bring them over on the morrow. "You are certain that is the earliest?" he said.

She was certain, with a marked coldness.

"I should explain," he added, "what I was really too cold

15 and fatigued to do before, that I am an experimental investigator."

"Indeed, sir," said Mrs. Hall, much impressed.

"And my baggage contains apparatus and appliances."

"Very useful things indeed they are, sir," said Mrs.

20 Hall.

"And I'm naturally anxious to get on with my inquiries."

"Of course, sir."

"My reason for coming to Iping," he proceeded, with a

25 certain deliberation of manner, "was – a desire for soli-

---

11 **morrow** (arch.): Morgen.
15 **fatigued:** müde.
15f. **investigator:** Forscher.
18 **appliance:** Gerät, Hilfsmittel.
21 **to be anxious to do s.th.:** bestrebt, eifrig bemüht sein, etwas zu tun.
21f. **inquiry:** Untersuchung, Forschung(sarbeit).
25 **deliberation:** Nachdenklichkeit, Bedächtigkeit.
25f. **solitude:** Einsamkeit, Alleinsein.

tude. I do not wish to be disturbed in my work. In addition to my work, an accident —"

"I thought as much," said Mrs. Hall to herself.

"– necessitates a certain retirement. My eyes – are sometimes so weak and painful that I have to shut myself up in the dark for hours together. Lock myself up. Sometimes – now and then. Not at present, certainly. At such times the slightest disturbance, the entry of a stranger into the room, is a source of excruciating annoyance to me – it is well these things should be understood."

"Certainly, sir," said Mrs. Hall. "And if I might make so bold as to ask —"

"That, I think, is all," said the stranger, with that quietly irresistible air of finality he could assume at will. Mrs. Hall reserved her question and sympathy for a better occasion.

After Mrs. Hall had left the room, he remained standing in front of the fire, glaring, so Mr. Henfrey puts it, at the clock-mending. Mr. Henfrey not only took off the hands of the clock, and the face, but extracted the works; and he tried to work in as slow and quiet and unassuming a manner as possible. He worked with the lamp close to him, and the green shade threw a brilliant light upon his

---

4 **to necessitate:** notwendig, erforderlich machen.
9 **excruciating:** unerträglich.
14 **irresistible:** unwiderstehlich.
   finality: Endgültigkeit, Entschiedenheit.
18 **to glare at s.th.:** etwas anstarren, mit finsterer Miene bei etwas zusehen.
20 **face:** Zifferblatt.
   to extract: herausnehmen, entfernen.
   works (pl.): Uhrwerk.
21 **unassuming:** unauffällig.
23 **shade:** *lamp-shade:* Lampenschirm.

hands, and upon the frame and wheels, and left the rest
of the room shadowy. When he looked up, coloured
patches swam in his eyes. Being constitutionally of a curious nature, he had removed the works – a quite unnecessary proceeding – with the idea of delaying his de-
parture and perhaps falling into conversation with
the stranger. But the stranger stood there, perfectly silent and still. So still, it got on Henfrey's nerves. He felt
alone in the room and looked up, and there, grey and
dim, was the bandaged head and huge blue lenses staring fixedly, with a mist of green spots drifting in front
of them. It was so uncanny-looking to Henfrey that for a
minute they remained staring blankly at one another.
Then Henfrey looked down again. Very uncomfortable
position! One would like to say something. Should he
remark that the weather was very cold for the time of
year?

He looked up as if to take aim with that introductory
shot. "The weather" – he began.

"Why don't you finish and go?" said the rigid figure, evidently in a state of painfully suppressed rage. "All
you've got to do is to fix the hour-hand on its axle.
You're simply humbugging —"

---

3 **constitutionally** (adv.): von Natur aus.
5 **proceeding**: Prozedur.
10 **lens**: Linse, Augenglas.
11 **fixedly** (adv.): starr.
12 **uncanny-looking**: unheimlich aussehend.
13 **blankly** (adv.): verdutzt; ausdrucksleer.
18 **to take aim**: zielen.
    introductory: einleitend.
21 **painfully suppressed rage**: mühsam unterdrückte Wut.
22 **axle**: Achse.
23 **to humbug**: Unfug treiben.

"Certainly, sir – one minute more, sir. I overlooked –"
And Mr. Henfrey finished and went.

But he went off feeling excessively annoyed. "Damn it!"
said Mr. Henfrey to himself, trudging down the village
5 through the thawing snow; "a man must do a clock at
times, sure-lie."

And again: "Can't a man look at you? – Ugly!"

And yet again: "Seemingly not. If the police was wanting
you you couldn't be more wropped and bandaged."

10 At Gleeson's corner he saw Hall, who had recently mar-
ried the stranger's hostess at the Coach and Horses, and
who now drove the Iping conveyance, when occasional
people required it, to Sidderbridge Junction, coming towards him on his return from that place. Hall had evi-
15 dently been "stopping a bit" at Sidderbridge, to judge by
his driving. "'Ow do, Teddy?" he said, passing.

"You got a rum un up home!" said Teddy.

Hall very sociably pulled up. "What's that?" he asked.

"Rum-looking customer stopping at the Coach and
20 Horses," said Teddy. "My sakes!"

And he proceeded to give Hall a vivid description of his
grotesque guest. "Looks a bit like a disguise, don't it? I'd
like to see a man's face if I had him stopping in *my*
place," said Henfrey. "But women are that trustful, –

---

4 **to trudge:** stapfen, mühsam gehen.
6 **sure-lie** (dial., adv.): *surely:* doch, wohl.
9 **wropped:** vermummt.
11 **hostess:** Wirtin.
12 **conveyance:** Personenkutsche, Postwagen.
13 **junction:** Kreuzung, Abzweigung.
16 **'ow do?** (dial.): *how do you do?*
17 **a rum un** (slang, dial.): *a rum one:* ein komischer Kauz.
18 **sociably** (adv.): gesellig, leutselig, aufgeschlossen.
    to pull up: anhalten, haltmachen.

where strangers are concerned. He's took your rooms
and he ain't even given a name, Hall."

"You don't say so!" said Hall, who was a man of sluggish
apprehension.

5 "Yes," said Teddy. "By the week. Whatever he is, you
can't get rid of him under the week. And he's got a lot of
luggage coming to-morrow, so he says. Let's hope it
won't be stones in boxes, Hall."

He told Hall how his aunt at Hastings had been swindled
10 by a stranger with empty portmanteaux. Altogether he
left Hall vaguely suspicious. "Get up, old girl," said Hall.
"I s'pose I must see 'bout this."

Teddy trudged on his way with his mind considerably relieved.

15 Instead of "seeing 'bout it," however, Hall on his return
was severely rated by his wife on the length of time he
had spent in Sidderbridge, and his mild inquiries were
answered snappishly and in a manner not to the point.
But the seed of suspicion Teddy had sown germinated in
20 the mind of Mr. Hall in spite of these discouragements.
"You wim' don't know everything," said Mr. Hall, resolved to ascertain more about the personality of his

---

3 **you don't say so!** (infml.): was du nicht sagst, kaum zu glauben.
   sluggish: langsam, träge.
4 **apprehension:** Auffassung(svermögen).
5 **by the week:** mit wöchentlicher Kündigung.
12 **s'pose** (dial.): *suppose.*
   to see about s.th.: sich eine Sache mal ansehen.
16 **to rate s.o.:** jdn. ausschelten.
18 **snappishly** (adv.): schnippisch, bissig.
   not to the point (adv.): ausweichend.
19 **to germinate:** (fig.) aufkeimen.
20 **discouragement:** Entmutigung.
21 **wim'** (dial.): *women.*
22 **to ascertain:** in Erfahrung bringen.

guest at the earliest possible opportunity. And after the
stranger had gone to bed, which he did about half-past
nine, Mr. Hall went aggressively into the parlour and
looked very hard at his wife's furniture, just to show that
5 the stranger wasn't master there, and scrutinised closely
and a little contemptuously a sheet of mathematical
computation the stranger had left. When retiring for the
night he instructed Mrs. Hall to look very closely at the
stranger's luggage when it came next day.

10 "You mind your own business, Hall," said Mrs. Hall,
"and I'll mind mine."

She was all the more inclined to snap at Hall because the
stranger was undoubtedly an unusually strange sort of
stranger, and she was by no means assured about him in
15 her own mind. In the middle of the night she woke up
dreaming of huge white heads like turnips, that came
trailing after her at the end of interminable necks, and
with vast black eyes. But being a sensible woman, she
subdued her terrors and turned over and went to sleep
20 again.

---

5 **to scrutinise:** mustern, genau anschauen.
7 **computation:** Berechnungen.
10 **to mind one's own business:** sich um die eigenen Angelegenheiten
kümmern.
12 **to be inclined to do s.th.:** dazu neigen, etwas zu tun.
  to snap at s.o.: jdn. anfauchen.
16 **turnip:** (Kohl-, Steck-)Rübe.
17 **to trail:** verfolgen.
  interminable: unendlich lang.
19 **to subdue:** (Gefühl) bezähmen, überwinden.

Chapter III

The Thousand and One Bottles

Thus it was that on the twenty-ninth day of February, at
the beginning of the thaw, this singular person fell out of
infinity into Iping Village. Next day his luggage arrived
through the slush. And very remarkable luggage it was.
There were a couple of trunks indeed, such as a rational
man might need, but in addition there were a box of
books, – big, fat books, of which some were just in an incomprehensible handwriting, – and a dozen or more
crates, boxes, and cases, containing objects packed in
straw, as it seemed to Hall, tugging with a casual curiosity at the straw – glass bottles. The stranger, muffled in
hat, coat, gloves, and wrapper, came out impatiently to
meet Fearenside's cart, while Hall was having a word or
so of gossip preparatory to helping bring them in. Out he
came, not noticing Fearenside's dog, who was sniffing in
a *dilettante* spirit at Hall's legs. "Come along with those
boxes," he said. "I've been waiting long enough."
And he came down the steps towards the tail of the cart
as if to lay hands on the smaller crate.
No sooner had Fearenside's dog caught sight of him, how-

---

4 **thaw:** Tauwetter.
   singular: merkwürdig.
6 **slush:** Schneematsch.
9f. **incomprehensible:** unverständlich.
11 **crate:** Kiste.
12 **casual:** zufällig, beiläufig.
14 **wrapper:** Umschlag, Hülle.
16 **preparatory to doing s.th.:** ehe man etwas tut.
17f. **in a dilettante spirit:** freundlich (*dilettante* [Fr.]: dilettantisch).

ever, than it began to bristle and growl savagely, and when
he rushed down the steps it gave an undecided hop, and
then sprang straight at his hand. "Whup!" cried Hall,
jumping back, for he was no hero with dogs, and Fearenside howled, "Lie down!" and snatched his whip.

They saw the dog's teeth had slipped the hand, heard a
kick, saw the dog execute a flanking jump and get home
on the stranger's leg, and heard the rip of his trousering.
Then the finer end of Fearenside's whip reached his
property, and the dog, yelping with dismay, retreated
under the wheels of the waggon. It was all the business
of a half-minute. No one spoke, every one shouted. The
stranger glanced swiftly at his torn glove and at his leg,
made as if he would stoop to the latter, then turned and
rushed up the steps into the inn. They heard him go
headlong across the passage and up the uncarpeted
stairs to his bedroom.

"You brute, you!" said Fearenside, climbing off the waggon with his whip in his hand, while the dog watched him
through the wheel. "Come here!" said Fearenside –
"You'd better."

Hall had stood gaping. "He wuz bit," said Hall. "I'd

---

1 **to bristle:** sich sträuben (Haare).
3 **whup!** (dial.): *whoop:* Ausruf der Aufregung; etwa: holla!
6 **to slip:** loslassen.
7 **flanking jump:** Sprung zur Seite.
7f. **to get home on the stranger's leg:** etwa: sich in das Bein des Fremden verbeißen (*to get home:* das Ziel erreichen).
8 **rip:** Reißen, Riß.
10 **property:** hier: Ziel.
   to yelp with dismay: erschreckt heulen, kläffen (*dismay:* Schrecken).
16 **headlong** (adv.): geradeaus; blindlings.
18 **brute:** Vieh.
22 **he wuz bit** (dial.): *he was bitten.*

better go and see to en," and he trotted after the
stranger. He met Mrs. Hall in the passage. "Carrier's
darg," he said, "bit en."
He went straight upstairs, and the stranger's door be-
5 ing ajar, he pushed it open and was entering without
any ceremony, being of a naturally sympathetic turn of
mind.
The blind was down and the room dim. He caught a
glimpse of a most singular thing, what seemed a handless
10 arm waving towards him, and a face of three huge indeterminate spots on white, very like the face of a pale
pansy. Then he was struck violently in the chest, hurled
back, and the door slammed in his face and locked all so
rapidly that he had no time to observe. A waving of in-
15 decipherable shapes, a blow, and a concussion. There he
stood on the dark little landing, wondering what it might
be that he had seen.
After a couple of minutes he rejoined the little group
that had formed outside the Coach and Horses. There
20 was Fearenside telling about it all over again for the sec-

1 **en** (dial.): *him.*
3 **darg** (dial.): *dog.*
5 **ajar:** angelehnt, leicht geöffnet.
5f. **without any ceremony:** ohne jede Förmlichkeit.
6f. **sympathetic turn of mind:** mitfühlende Art.
10f. **indeterminate:** unbestimmt.
12 **pansy:** Stiefmütterchen.
12f. **to be hurled back:** heftig zurückgestoßen werden.
13 **to slam:** zuschlagen, zuknallen (Tür).
14 **waving:** hier: Ineinanderfließen.
14f. **indecipherable:** rätselhaft.
15 **concussion:** hier: Zusammenstoß, Erschütterung.
16 **landing:** Treppenabsatz; Hausflur.
18 **to rejoin:** sich wieder (zu etwas) gesellen.

ond time; there was Mrs. Hall saying his dog didn't have
no business to bite her guests; there was Huxter, the general dealer from over the road, interrogative; and Sandy
Wadgers from the forge, judicial; besides women and
children, – all of them saying fatuities: "Wouldn't let en
bite *me*, I knows;" "'Tasn't right *have* such dargs;"
"Whad 'e bite'n for then?" and so forth.

Mr. Hall, staring at them from the steps and listening,
found it incredible that he had seen anything very remarkable happen upstairs. Besides, his vocabulary was
altogether too limited to express his impressions.

"He don't want no help, he says," he said in answer to his
wife's inquiry. "We'd better be a-takin' of his luggage
in."

"He ought to have it cauterised at once," said Mr. Huxter; "especially if it's at all inflamed."

"I'd shoot en, that's what I'd do," said a lady in the
group.

Suddenly the dog began growling again.

"Come along," cried an angry voice in the doorway, and

1f. **didn't have no business** (dial.): *didn't have any business.*
2f. **general dealer:** Krämer.
3 **interrogative:** Fragen stellend.
4 **forge:** Schmiede.
   judicial: kritisch, unvoreingenommen; hier auch: auf alles eine Ant-
   wort wissend.
5 **fatuity:** albernes Zeug, unsinnige Bemerkung.
6 **I knows** (dial.): *I know.*
   'Tasn't right have such dargs (dial.): *It isn't right to have such dogs.*
7 **What 'e bite'n for then?** (dial.): *What did he bite him for then?*
12 **he don't** (dial.): *he doesn't.*
13 **a-takin' of** (dial.): *taking.*
15 **to cauterise:** (Wunde) ausbrennen.
16 **inflamed:** entzündet.

there stood the muffled stranger with his collar turned
up, and his hat-brim bent down. "The sooner you get
those things in the better I'll be pleased." It is stated by
an anonymous bystander that his trousers and gloves
5 had been changed.

"Was you hurt, sir?" said Fearenside. "I'm rare sorry the
darg —"

"Not a bit," said the stranger. "Never broke the skin.
Hurry up with those things."

10 He then swore to himself, so Mr. Hall asserts.

Directly the first crate was carried into the parlour, in
accordance with his directions, the stranger flung himself upon it with extraordinary eagerness, and began
to unpack it, scattering the straw with an utter disregard
15 of Mrs. Hall's carpet. And from it he began to produce
bottles, – little fat bottles containing powders, small and
slender bottles containing coloured and white fluids,
fluted blue bottles labelled *Poison*, bottles with round
bodies and slender necks, large green-glass bottles,
20 large white-glass bottles, bottles with glass stoppers
and frosted labels, bottles with fine corks, bottles with
bungs, bottles with wooden caps, wine bottles, salad-oil
bottles, – putting them in rows on the chiffonnier, on the

---

6 **rare:** *rarely* (adv.): außergewöhnlich.
10 **to assert:** behaupten.
11 f. **in accordance with:** entsprechend.
12 **direction:** Anweisung, Befehl.
17 **fluid:** Flüssigkeit.
18 **fluted:** langhalsig, schlank.
    to label s.th.: etwas mit einem Etikett, einer Aufschrift versehen.
20 **stopper:** Stöpsel.
21 **frosted:** 1. gebleicht, matt; 2. angeätzt.
22 **bung:** Spund(zapfen).
24 **chiffonnier** (Fr.): Kommode.

mantel, on the table under the window, round the floor, on the book-shelf, – everywhere. The chemist's shop in Bramblehurst could not boast half so many. Quite a sight it was. Crate after crate yielded bottles, until all six were empty and the table high with straw; the only things that came out of these crates besides the bottles were a number of test-tubes and a carefully packed balance.

And directly the crates were unpacked, the stranger went to the window and set to work, not troubling in the least about the litter of straw, the fire which had gone out, the box of books outside, nor for the trunks and other luggage that had gone upstairs.

When Mrs. Hall took his dinner in to him, he was already so absorbed in his work, pouring little drops out of the bottles into test-tubes, that he did not hear her until she had swept away the bulk of the straw and put the tray on the table, with some little emphasis perhaps, seeing the state that the floor was in. Then he half turned his head and immediately turned it away again. But she saw he had removed his glasses; they were beside him on the table, and it seemed to her that his eye sockets were extraordinarily hollow. He put on his spectacles again, and then turned and faced her. She

1 **mantel:** Kaminsims.
2f. **chemist's shop:** Apotheke.
3 **to boast s.th.:** etwas sein eigen nennen.
4 **to yield:** hervorbringen, herausgeben.
7 **test-tube:** Reagenzglas.
8 **balance:** Waage.
11 **litter:** Unordnung.
17 **bulk:** größter Teil, Großteil.
23 **eyesocket:** Augenhöhle.

was about to complain of the straw on the floor when he anticipated her.

"I wish you wouldn't come in without knocking," he said in the tone of abnormal exasperation that seemed so characteristic of him.

"I knocked, but seemingly —"

"Perhaps you did. But in my investigations – my really very urgent and necessary investigations – the slightest disturbance, the jar of a door – I must ask you —"

"Certainly, sir. You can turn the lock if you're like that, you know, – any time."

"A very good idea," said the stranger.

"This stror, sir, if I might make so bold as to remark —"

"Don't. If the straw makes trouble put it down in the bill." And he mumbled at her – words suspiciously like curses.

He was so odd, standing there, so aggressive and explosive, bottle in one hand and test-tube in the other, that Mrs. Hall was quite alarmed. But she was a resolute woman. "In which case, I should like to know, sir, what you consider —"

"A shilling. Put down a shilling. Surely a shilling's enough?"

"So be it," said Mrs. Hall, taking up the table-cloth and beginning to spread it over the table. "If you're satisfied, of course —"

---

2 **to anticipate s.o.:** jdm. zuvorkommen.
4 **exasperation:** Gereiztheit.
9 **jar:** Knarren.
13 **stror** (dial.): *straw.*
16 **to mumble at s.o.:** jdn. anbrummeln.

He turned and sat down, with his coat-collar towards her.

All the afternoon he worked with the door locked and, as Mrs. Hall testifies, for the most part in silence. But once there was a concussion and a sound of bottles ringing together as though the table had been hit, and the smash of a bottle flung violently down, and then a rapid pacing athwart the room. Fearing "something was the matter," she went to the door and listened, not caring to knock.

"I can't go on," he was raving. "I *can't* go on. Three hundred thousand, four hundred thousand! The huge multitude! Cheated! All my life it may take me! Patience! Patience indeed! Fool and liar!"

There was a noise of hobnails on the bricks in the bar, and Mrs. Hall very reluctantly had to leave the rest of his soliloquy. When she returned the room was silent again, save for the faint crepitation of his chair and the occasional clink of a bottle. It was all over. The stranger had resumed work.

When she took in his tea she saw broken glass in the corner of the room under the concave mirror, and a golden

---

4 **to testify:** bezeugen, aussagen.
7 **smash:** Zerbersten, Zersplittern.
8 **athwart:** quer durch.
11 **to rave:** wüten, rasen.
12f. **multitude:** Menge.
15 **hobnail:** Schuhnagel.
16 **reluctantly** (adv.): widerwillig, widerstrebend.
17 **soliloquy:** Selbstgespräch.
18 **save for:** ausgenommen, mit Ausnahme von.
   crepitation: Knarren.
19 **clink:** Klirren.
22 **concave mirror:** Hohlspiegel.

stain that had been carelessly wiped. She called attention to it.

"Put it down in the bill," snapped her visitor. "For God's
sake don't worry me. If there's damage done, put it down
in the bill;" and he went on ticking a list in the exercise
book before him.

"I'll tell you something," said Fearenside, mysteriously.
It was late in the afternoon, and they were in the little
beer-shop of Iping Hanger.

"Well?" said Teddy Henfrey.

"This chap you're speaking of, what my dog bit. Well –
he's black. Leastways, his legs are. I seed through the
tear of his trousers and the tear of his glove. You'd have
expected a sort of pinky to show, wouldn't you? Well –
there wasn't none. Just blackness. I tell you, he's as black
as my hat."

"My sakes!" said Henfrey. "It's a rummy case altogether.
Why, his nose is as pink as paint!"

"That's true," said Fearenside. "I knows that. And I
tell 'e what I'm thinking. That marn's a piebald, Teddy.
Black here and white there – in patches. And he's
ashamed of it. He's a kind of half-breed, and the colour's

---

5 **to tick a list:** die Posten einer Liste abhaken, mit einem Zeichen versehen.
11 **what my dog bit** (dial.): *whom my dog bit; who was bitten by my dog.*
12 **leastways** (adv., infml.): zumindest.
I seed (dial.): *I saw.*
17 **rummy** (slang): komisch, seltsam.
20 **'e** (dial.): *ye: you.*
marn (dial.): *man.*
piebald: Schecke.
22 **half-breed:** Mischblut.

come off patchy instead of mixing. I've heard of such
things before. And it's the common way with horses, as
any one can see."

Chapter IV

Mr. Cuss Interviews the Stranger

I have told the circumstances of the stranger's arrival in
Iping with a certain fulness of detail, in order that the curious impression he created may be understood by the
reader. But excepting two odd incidents, the circumstances of his stay until the extraordinary day of the
Club Festival may be passed over very cursorily. There
were a number of skirmishes with Mrs. Hall on matters
of domestic discipline, but in every case until late in
April, when the first signs of penury began, he over-rode
her by the easy expedient of an extra payment. Hall did
not like him, and whenever he dared he talked of the advisability of getting rid of him; but he showed his dislike
chiefly by concealing it ostentatiously, and avoiding his

---

1 **patchy:** fleckig, ungleichmäßig.
11 **cursorily** (adv.): flüchtig, oberflächlich.
12 **skirmish** (fig.): Geplänkel, Zusammenstoß.
14 **penury:** Geldknappheit.
14f. **to over-ride s.o.:** sich über jdn. hinwegsetzen; hier: jdn. beschwich-
tigen.
15 **expedient:** Mittel, Notbehelf.
16f. **advisability:** Ratsamkeit.
18 **to conceal:** verbergen.
   ostentatiously (adv.): absichtlich, deutlich.

visitor as much as possible. "Wait till the summer," said
Mrs. Hall, sagely, "when the artisks are beginning to
come. Then we'll see. He may be a bit overbearing, but
bills settled punctual is bills settled punctual, whatever
5 you like to say."
The stranger did not go to church, and indeed made no
difference between Sunday and the irreligious days,
even in costume. He worked, as Mrs. Hall thought, very
fitfully. Some days he would come down early and be
10 continuously busy. On others he would rise late, pace his
room, fretting audibly for hours together, smoke, sleep
in the arm-chair by the fire. Communication with the
world beyond the village he had none. His temper continued very uncertain; for the most part his manner was
15 that of a man suffering under almost unendurable pro-
vocation, and once or twice things were snapped, torn
crushed, or broken in spasmodic gusts of violence. He
seemed under a chronic irritation of the greatest inten-
sity. His habit of talking to himself in a low voice grew
20 steadily upon him, but though Mrs. Hall listened conscientiously she could make neither head nor tail of what
she heard.

2 **sagely** (adv.): verständig.
   artisks (dial.): *artists.*
3 **overbearing:** arrogant, herrisch.
7 **irreligious days:** Wochentage.
9 **fitfully** (adv.): unregelmäßig.
11 **to fret:** sich aufregen, ärgern.
17 **to crush:** zerquetschen, zermalmen.
   spasmodic: anfall-, krampfartig.
   gust: (fig.) Ausbruch.
19f. **to grow upon s.o.:** bei jdm. zunehmen.
20f. **conscientiously** (adv.): genau, gewissenhaft.
21 **to make neither head nor tail of s.th.:** aus einer Sache nicht schlau
   werden.

He rarely went abroad by daylight, but at twilight he would go out muffled up enormously, whether the weather were cold or not, and he chose the loneliest paths and those most over-shadowed by trees and banks. His goggling spectacles and ghastly bandaged face under the penthouse of his hat, came with a disagreeable suddenness out of the darkness upon one or two home-going labourers; and Teddy Henfrey, tumbling out of the Scarlet Coat one night at half-past nine, was scared shamefully by the stranger's skull-like head (he was walking hat in hand) lit by the sudden light of the opened inn door. Such children as saw him at nightfall dreamt of bogies, and it seemed doubtful whether he disliked boys more than they disliked him, or the reverse, – but there was certainly a vivid enough dislike on either side.

It was inevitable that a person of so remarkable an appearance and bearing should form a frequent topic in such a village as Iping. Opinion was greatly divided about his occupation. Mrs. Hall was sensitive on the point. When questioned, she explained very carefully that he was an "experimental investigator," going gingerly over the syllables as one who dreads pitfalls. When

---

4 **bank:** Böschung.
5 **ghastly:** schrecklich, gespenstisch, schaurig, schauderhaft.
6 **penthouse:** (fig.) Überdachung, Vorsprung.
9 **the Scarlet Coat:** Name eines Gasthauses (*scarlet:* scharlachrot).
10 **shamefully** (adv.): auf beschämende Weise.
13 **bogy:** (Schreck-)Gespenst.
14f. **reverse:** Gegenteil.
17 **inevitable:** unvermeidlich.
18 **bearing:** Betragen, Benehmen.
22f. **gingerly** (adv.): sachte, behutsam.
23 **pitfall:** (fig.) Falle.

asked what an experimental investigator was, she would
say with a touch of superiority that most educated people knew that, and would then explain that he "discovered things." Her visitor had had an accident, she said,
5 which temporarily discoloured his face and hands; and
being of a sensitive disposition, he was averse to any
public notice of the fact.

Out of her hearing there was a view largely entertained
that he was a criminal trying to escape from justice by
10 wrapping himself up so as to conceal himself altogether
from the eye of the police. This idea sprang from the
brain of Mr. Teddy Henfrey. No crime of any magnitude
dating from the middle or end of February was known to
have occurred. Elaborated in the imagination of Mr.
15 Gould, the probationary assistant in the National
School, this theory took the form that the stranger was
an Anarchist in disguise, preparing explosives, and he
resolved to undertake such detective operations as his
time permitted. These consisted for the most part in
20 looking very hard at the stranger whenever they met, or
in asking people who had never seen the stranger, leading questions about him. But he detected nothing.

Another school of opinion followed Mr. Fearenside, and

---

5 **temporarily** (adv.): zeitweilig, vorübergehend.
6 **to be averse to s.th.:** einer Sache abgeneigt sein.
7 **notice:** Bekanntwerden.
8 **to entertain a view:** eine Ansicht vertreten.
12 **magnitude:** Ausmaß, Bedeutung, Größe.
14 **to elaborate s.th.:** etwas ausarbeiten, ausklügeln, Gestalt werden lassen.
15 **probationary assistant:** Probelehrer.
15f. **National School:** Grund-, Hauptschule.
22 **to detect:** ent-, aufdecken.

either accepted the piebald view or some modification
of it; as, for instance, Silas Durgan, who was heard to assert that "if he choses to show enself at fairs he'd make
his fortune in no time," and being a bit of a theologian,
5 compared the stranger to the man with the one talent.
Yet another view explained the entire matter by regarding the stranger as a harmless lunatic. That had the advantage of accounting for everything straight away.
Between these main groups there were waverers and
10 compromisers. Sussex folk have few superstitions, and
it was only after the events of early April that the
thought of the supernatural was first whispered in the
village. Even then it was only credited among the
women folks.
15 But whatever they thought of him, people in Iping
on the whole agreed in disliking him. His irritability,
though it might have been comprehensible to an urban
brain-worker, was an amazing thing to these quiet Sussex villagers. The frantic gesticulations they surprised
20 now and then, the headlong pace after nightfall that
swept him upon them round quiet corners, the inhuman

---

1 **modification:** Abart.
3 **enself** (dial.): *himself.*
5 **talent:** altgriechische Geldeinheit.
7 **lunatic:** Irrer, Verrückter.
8 **to account for s.th.:** etwas erklären.
9 **waverer:** Zauderer (von *to waver* ›schwanken, unschlüssig sein‹).
10 **superstition:** Aberglaube.
12 **the supernatural:** das Übernatürliche.
13 **to credit s.th.:** etwas Glauben schenken.
16 **irritability:** Reizbarkeit.
17 **urban:** städtisch.
19 **frantic:** wild.
20 **headlong:** ungestüm, hastig.

bludgeoning of all the tentative advances of curiosity, the taste for twilight that led to the closing of doors, the pulling down of blinds, the extinction of candles and lamps, – who could agree with such goings on? They
5 drew aside as he passed down the village, and when he had gone by, young humourists would up with coat-collars and down with hat-brims, and go pacing nervously after him in imitation of his occult bearing. There was a song popular at that time called the "Bogey Man"; Miss
10 Statchell sang it at the schoolroom concert (in aid of the church lamps), and thereafter whenever one or two of the villagers were gathered together and the stranger appeared, a bar or so of this tune, more or less sharp or flat, was whistled in the midst of them. Also belated little
15 children would call "Bogey Man!" after him, and make off tremulously elated.

Cuss, the general practitioner, was devoured by curiosity. The bandages excited his professional interest, the report of the thousand and one bottles aroused his jeal-
20 ous regard. All through April and May he coveted an

---

1 **bludgeoning:** (fig.) grobe Zurückweisung (von *to bludgeon* ›niederknüppeln‹).
 tentative: vorsichtig, zögernd.
3 **extinction:** Auslöschen.
6 **humourist:** Spaßvogel.
8 **occult:** geheimnisvoll.
9 **bogey man:** Schreckgestalt, schwarzer Mann.
10 **in aid of s.th.:** zugunsten (der Anschaffung) von etwas.
13 **bar:** Takt (Musik).
14 **belated:** verspätet.
16 **tremulously** (adv.): zitternd.
 elated: freudig erregt.
17 **general practitioner:** praktischer Arzt.
 to be devoured by s.th.: (fig.) von etwas verzehrt werden.
20 **to covet s.th.:** begierig auf etwas sein.

opportunity of talking to the stranger; and at last, towards Whitsuntide, he could stand it no longer, and hit upon the subscription-list for a village nurse as an excuse. He was surprised to find that Mr. Hall did not know his guest's name. "He give a name," said Mrs. Hall, – an assertion which was quite unfounded, – "but I didn't rightly hear it." She thought it seemed so silly not to know the man's name.

Cuss rapped at the parlour door and entered. There was a fairly audible imprecation from within. "Pardon my intrusion," said Cuss, and then the door closed and cut Mrs. Hall off from the rest of the conversation.

She could hear the murmur of voices for the next ten minutes, then a cry of surprise, a stirring of feet, a chair flung aside, a bark of laughter, quick steps to the door, and Cuss appeared, his face white, his eyes staring over his shoulder. He left the door open behind him, and without looking at her strode across the hall and went down the steps, and she heard his feet hurrying along the road. He carried his hat in his hand. She stood behind the door, looking at the open door of the parlour. Then she heard the stranger laughing quietly, and then his footsteps came across the room. She could not see his face where she stood. The parlour door slammed, and the place was silent again.

Cuss went straight up the village to Bunting the vicar. "Am I mad?" Cuss began abruptly, as he entered

---

2 **Whitsuntide:** Pfingsten.
3 **subscription-list:** Spendenliste.
5 **he give** (dial.): *he gave.*
6 **unfounded:** ungerechtfertigt.
10 **imprecation:** Verwünschung, Fluch.

the shabby little study. "Do I look like an insane person?"

"What's happened?" said the vicar, putting the ammonite on the loose sheets of his forthcoming sermon.

5 "That chap at the inn —"

"Well?"

"Give me something to drink," said Cuss, and he sat down.

When his nerves had been steadied by a glass of cheap
10 sherry, – the only drink the good vicar had available, – he told him of the interview he had just had. "Went in," he gasped, "and began to demand a subscription for that Nurse Fund. He'd stuck his hands in his pockets as I came in, and he sat down lumpily in his chair. Sniffed. I
15 told him I'd heard he took an interest in scientific things. He said yes. Sniffed again. Kept on sniffing all the time; evidently recently caught an infernal cold. No wonder, wrapped up like that! I developed the nurse idea, and all the while kept my eyes open. Bottles – chemicals –
20 everywhere. Balance, test-tubes in stands, and a smell of – evening primrose. Would he subscribe? Said he'd con-

---

1 **shabby:** armselig.
  insane: verrückt, wahnsinnig.
3 f. **ammonite:** Ammonit (spiralförmige Versteinerung eines ausgestorbenen Kopffüßers).
4 **forthcoming:** bevorstehend.
5 **chap** (infml.): Kerl, Typ.
10 **to have s.th. available:** etwas vorrätig, im Haus haben.
13 **fund:** Fond.
14 **lumpily** (adv.): schwer(fällig).
  to sniff: schnüffeln, niesen.
17 **infernal:** höllisch, schrecklich.
21 **evening primrose:** Nachtkerze (Blume).
  to subscribe: unterzeichnen; zusichern, etwas zu spenden.

sider it. Asked him, point-blank, was he researching.
Said he was. A long research? Got quite cross. 'A damnable long research,' said he, blowing the cork out, so to
speak. 'Oh,' said I. And out came the grievance. The
man was just on the boil, and my question boiled him
over. He had been given a prescription, most valuable
prescription – what for he wouldn't say. Was it medical?
'Damn you! What are you fishing after?' I apologised.
Dignified sniff and cough. He resumed. He'd read it.
Five ingredients. Put it down; turned his head. Draught
of air from window lifted the paper. Swish, rustle. He
was working in a room with an open fireplace, he said.
Saw a flicker, and there was the prescription burning and
lifting chimneyward. Rushed towards it just as it
whisked up chimney. So! Just at that point, to illustrate
his story, out came his arm."

"Well?"

"No hand, – just an empty sleeve. Lord! I thought, *that's*
a deformity! Got a cork arm, I suppose, and has taken it
off. Then, I thought, there's something odd in that. What

---

1 **point-blank** (adv.): rundheraus.
  to research: forschen, experimentieren.
2f. **damnable:** verdammt.
3 **to blow the cork out** (fig.): die Sache herauslassen.
4 **grievance:** Verdruß.
5 **the be on the boil:** (fig.) am Siedepunkt sein.
6 **prescription:** (Arznei-)Rezept.
8 **to fish after s.th.:** auf etwas aussein.
9 **dignified:** würdig, würdevoll.
10 **ingredient:** Bestandteil.
11 **swish:** Zischen.
13 **flicker:** Aufflackern.
14 **chimneyward** (adv.): kaminwärts.
19 **deformity:** Mißbildung.

the devil keeps that sleeve up and open, if there's nothing in it? There was nothing in it, I tell you. Nothing
down it, right down to the joint. I could see right down it
to the elbow, and there was a glimmer of light shining
5 through a tear of the cloth. 'Good God!' I said. Then he
stopped. Stared at me with those black goggles of his,
and then at his sleeve."

"Well?"

"That's all. He never said a word; just glared, and put his
10 sleeve back in his pocket quickly. 'I was saying,' said he,
'that there was the prescription burning, wasn't I?' Interrogative cough. 'How the devil,' said I, 'can you move an
empty sleeve like that?' 'Empty sleeve?' 'Yes,' said I, 'an
empty sleeve.'

15 'It's an empty sleeve, is it? You saw it was an empty
sleeve?' He stood up right away. I stood up too. He came
towards me in three very slow steps, and stood quite
close. Sniffed venomously. I didn't flinch, though I'm
hanged if that bandaged knob of his, and those blinkers,
20 aren't enough to unnerve any one, coming quietly up to
you.

'You said it was an empty sleeve?' he said. 'Certainly,' I
said. At staring and saying nothing a barefaced man, unspectacled, starts scratch. Then very quietly he pulled his
25 sleeve out of his pocket again, and raised his arm to-

---

3 **joint:** Gelenk.
4 **glimmer:** Schimmer.
18 **venomously** (adv.): giftig, boshaft.
   to flinch: zurückzucken.
18f. **I'm hanged if:** ich will verflucht sein, wenn …
19 **knob:** hier: Kopf.
   blinkers: Glotzaugen.
20 **to unnerve:** entnerven, erschüttern, zermürben.

wards me as though he would show it to me again. He
did it very, very slowly. I looked at it. Seemed an age.
'Well?' said I, clearing my throat, 'there's nothing in it.'
Had to say something. I was beginning to feel fright-
5 ened. I could see right down it. He extended it straight
towards me, slowly, slowly, – just like that, – until the cuff
was six inches from my face. Queer thing to see an empty
sleeve come at you like that! And then —"
"Well?"
10 "Something – exactly like a finger and thumb it felt –
nipped my nose."
Bunting began to laugh.
"There wasn't anything there!" said Cuss, his voice running up into a shriek at the "there." "It's all very well for
15 you to laugh, but I tell you I was so startled, I hit his cuff
hard, and turned round, and cut out of the room – I left
him —"
Cuss stopped. There was no mistaking the sincerity of
his panic. He turned round in a helpless way and took a
20 second glass of the excellent vicar's very inferior sherry.
"When I hit his cuff," said Cuss, "I tell you, it felt exactly
like hitting an arm. And there wasn't an arm! There
wasn't the ghost of an arm!"
Mr. Bunting thought it over. He looked suspiciously at
25 Cuss. "It's a most remarkable story," he said. He looked
very wise and grave indeed. "It's really," said Mr. Bunting with judicial emphasis, "a most remarkable story."

---

  6 **cuff:** Manschette.
 11 **to nip:** kneifen.
 16 **to cut:** sich davonmachen.
 18 **sincerity:** Echtheit.
 20 **inferior:** mittelmäßig.
 27 **judicial:** richterlich.

Chapter V

The Burglary at the Vicarage

The facts of the burglary at the vicarage came to us
chiefly through the medium of the vicar and his wife. It
occurred in the small hours of Whit-Monday, – the day
devoted in Iping to the Club festivities. Mrs. Bunting, it
seems, woke up suddenly in the stillness that comes before the dawn, with the strong impression that the door
of their bedroom had opened and closed. She did not
arouse her husband at first, but sat up in bed listening.
She then distinctly heard the pad, pad, pad of bare feet
coming out of the adjoining dressing-room and walking
along the passage towards the staircase. As soon as she
felt assured of this, she aroused the Rev. Mr. Bunting as
quietly as possible. He did not strike a light, but putting
on his spectacles, her dressing-gown, and his bath slippers, he went out on the landing to listen. He heard quite
distinctly a fumbling going on at his study desk downstairs, and then a violent sneeze.
At that he returned to his bedroom, armed himself with

2 **burglary:** Einbruch (in ein Gebäude).
  vicarage: Pfarrhaus.
5 **small hours:** frühe Morgenstunden.
  Whit-Monday: Pfingstmontag.
6 (*to be*) **devoted to s.th.:** einer Sache gewidmet sein.
11 **pad:** Tappen, tappendes Geräusch.
12 **adjoining:** angrenzend, benachbart.
  dressing-room: Ankleidezimmer.
16 **dressing-gown:** Morgenrock.
16f. **slipper:** Pantoffel.
18 **to fumble:** herumtasten.
19 **sneeze:** Niesen.

the most obvious weapon, the poker, and descended the
staircase as noiselessly as possible. Mrs. Bunting came
out on the landing.

The hour was about four, and the ultimate darkness of
5 the night was past. There was a faint shimmer of light in
the hall, but the study doorway yawned impenetrably
black. Everything was still except the faint creaking of
the stairs under Mr. Bunting's tread, and the slight movements in the study. Then something snapped, the drawer
10 was opened, and there was a rustle of papers. Then came
an imprecation, and a match was struck and the study
was flooded with yellow light. Mr. Bunting was now in
the hall, and through the crack of the door he could see
the desk and the open drawer and a candle burning on
15 the desk. But the robber he could not see. He stood
there in the hall undecided what to do, and Mrs. Bunting, her face white and intent, crept slowly downstairs
after him. One thing kept up Mr. Bunting's courage:
the persuasion that this burglar was a resident in the
20 village.

They heard the chink of money, and realised that the
robber had found the housekeeping reserve of gold, –
two pounds ten in half-sovereigns altogether. At that
sound Mr. Bunting was nerved to abrupt action. Grip-
25 ping the poker firmly, he rushed into the room, closely

1 **poker:** Feuerzange.
4 **ultimate:** (fig.) tiefste(r, -s).
13 **crack:** Spalt.
17 **intent:** gespannt horchend.
19 **persuasion:** Überzeugung.
21 **chink:** Klimpern, Klirren.
22 **housekeeping reserve:** Wirtschafts-, Haushaltsgeld.
24 **nerved:** ermutigt.

followed by Mrs. Bunting. "Surrender!" cried Mr. Bunting, fiercely, and then stopped amazed. Apparently the room was perfectly empty.

Yet their conviction that they had, that very moment, heard somebody moving in the room had amounted to a certainty. For half a minute, perhaps, they stood gaping, then Mrs. Bunting went across the room and looked behind the screen, while Mr. Bunting, by a kindred impulse, peered under the desk. Then Mrs. Bunting turned back the window-curtains, and Mr. Bunting looked up the chimney and probed it with the poker. Then Mrs. Bunting scrutinised the waste-paper basket and Mr. Bunting opened the lid of the coal-scuttle. Then they came to a stop and stood with eyes interrogating each other.

"I could have sworn –" said Mr. Bunting.

"The candle!" said Mr. Bunting. "Who lit the candle?"

"The drawer!" said Mrs. Bunting. "And the money's gone!"

She went hastily to the doorway.

"Of all the extraordinary occurrences —"

There was a violent sneeze in the passage. They rushed out, and as they did so the kitchen door slammed. "Bring the candle," said Mr. Bunting, and led the way. They both heard a sound of bolts being hastily shot back.

As he opened the kitchen door he saw through the scul-

---

5 **to amount to s.th.:** (fig.) auf etwas hinauslaufen.
8 **screen:** Ofenschirm.
  kindred: verwandt, ähnlich.
11 **to probe:** untersuchen.
13 **coal-scuttle:** Kohlenständer, -eimer.
21 **occurrence:** Ereignis.
25 **to shoot back a bolt:** einen Türriegel zurückschieben.
26f. **scullery:** Spülküche.

lery that the back door was just opening, and the faint
light of early dawn displayed the dark masses of the garden beyond. He is certain that nothing went out of the
door. It opened, stood open for a moment, and then
5 closed with a slam. As it did so, the candle Mrs. Bunting
was carrying from the study flickered and flared. It was
a minute or more before they entered the kitchen.

The place was empty. They refastened the back door, examined the kitchen, pantry, and scullery thoroughly, and
10 at last went down into the cellar. There was not a soul to
be found in the house, search as they would.

Daylight found the vicar and his wife, a quaintly-costumed little couple, still marvelling about on their own
ground floor by the unnecessary light of a guttering
15 candle.

Chapter VI

The Furniture that went Mad

Now it happened that in the early hours of Whit-Monday, before Millie was hunted out for the day, Mr. Hall
20 and Mrs. Hall both rose and went noiselessly down into
the cellar. Their business there was of a private nature,

---

5 **slam:** Knall.
6 **to flare:** flackern, auflodern.
9 **pantry:** Speisekammer.
  thoroughly (adv.): gründlich.
12f. **quaintly-costumed:** seltsam gekleidet.
14 **to gutter:** flackern (Flamme); tropfen (Kerze).

and had something to do with the specific gravity of their
beer. They had hardly entered the cellar when Mrs. Hall
found she had forgotten to bring down a bottle of sarsaparilla from their joint room. As she was the expert
5 and principal operator in this affair, Hall very properly
went upstairs for it.
On the landing he was surprised to see that the stranger's
door was ajar. He went on into his own room and found
the bottle as he had been directed.
10 But returning with the bottle, he noticed that the bolts of
the front door had been shot back, that the door was in
fact simply on the latch. And with a flash of inspiration
he connected this with the stranger's room upstairs and
the suggestions of Mr. Teddy Henfrey. He distinctly re-
15 membered holding the candle while Mrs. Hall shot these
bolts overnight. At the sight he stopped, gaping, then
with the bottle still in his hand went upstairs again. He
rapped at the stranger's door. There was no answer. He
rapped again; then pushed the door wide open and en-
20 tered.
It was as he expected. The bed, the room also, was empty.
And what was stranger, even to his heavy intelligence,
on the bedroom chair and along the rail of the bed were
scattered the garments, the only garments so far as he
25 knew, and the bandages of their guest. His big slouch hat
even was cocked jauntily over the bed-post.

---

1 **specific gravity:** spezifisches Gewicht.
3 f. **sarsaparilla:** Sarsaparillwurzel (Heilwurzextrakt).
4 **joint room:** gemeinsames Zimmer.
12 **to be on the latch:** nur eingeklinkt sein (Tür).
23 **rail:** Stange, (Bett-)Umrandung.
25 **slouch hat:** Schlapphut.
26 **to be cocked jauntily over s.th.:** nachlässig über etwas gestülpt sein.

As Hall stood there he heard his wife's voice coming out
of the depth of the cellar, with that rapid telescoping of
the syllables and interrogative cocking up of the final
words to a high note, by which the West Sussex villager
is wont to indicate a brisk impatience. "Gearge! You gart
what a wand?"

At that he turned and hurried down to her. "Janny," he
said, over the rail of the cellar steps, " 'tas the truth what
Henfrey sez. 'E's not in uz room, 'e ent. And the front
door's unbolted."

At first Mrs. Hall did not understand, and as soon as she
did she resolved to see the empty room for herself. Hall,
still holding the bottle, went first. "If 'e ent there," he
said, "his close are. And what's 'e doin' without his close,
then? 'Tas a most curious basness."

As they came up the cellar steps, they both, it was afterwards ascertained, fancied they heard the front door
open and shut, but seeing it closed and nothing there,
neither said a word to the other about it at the time. Mrs.
Hall passed her husband in the passage and ran on first
upstairs. Some one sneezed on the staircase. Hall, following six steps behind, thought that he heard her
sneeze. She, going on first, was under the impression
that Hall was sneezing. She flung open the door and

---

2 **to telescope:** (fig.) zusammendrücken, -schieben.

3 f. **to cock up words to a high note:** den Tonfall verschärfen.

5 **to be wont to do s.th.:** etwas zu tun pflegen.
  brisk: forsch, eifrig, heftig, stark.

5 f. **Gearge! You gart what a wand?** (dial.): *George! You got what I
  want?*

8 f. **'Tas the truth what Henfrey sez. 'E's not in uz room, 'e ent** (dial.):
  What Henfrey says is the truth. He is not in his room, he isn't.

14 **close** (dial.): *clothes.*

15 **'Tas a most curious basness** (dial.): *It is a most curious business.*

stood regarding the room. "Of all the curious!" she
said.
She heard a sniff close behind her head as it seemed,
and, turning, was surprised to see Hall a dozen feet off
5 on the topmost stair. But in another moment he was
beside her. She bent forward and put her hand on the pillow and then under the clothes.
"Cold," she said. "He's been up this hour or more."
As she did so, a most extraordinary thing happened, –
10 the bed-clothes gathered themselves together, leapt up
suddenly into a sort of peak, and then jumped headlong
over the bottom rail. It was exactly as if a hand had
clutched them in the centre and flung them aside. Immediately after, the stranger's hat hopped off the bed-post,
15 described a whirling flight in the air through the better
part of a circle, and then dashed straight at Mrs. Hall's
face. Then as swiftly came the sponge from the washstand; and then the chair, flinging the stranger's coat and
trousers carelessly aside, and laughing drily in a voice
20 singularly like the stranger's, turned itself up with its
four legs at Mrs. Hall, seemed to take aim at her for a
moment, and charged at her. She screamed and turned,
and then the chair legs came gently but firmly against
her back and impelled her and Hall out of the room. The

---

1 **Of all the curious!:** *Of all the curious things I ever saw, this is the most*
strange.
10 **bed-clothes:** Bettücher.
11 **peak:** Spitze.
15 **to whirl:** wirbeln.
15f. **through the better part of a circle:** im Halbkreis.
17f. **washstand:** Waschtisch.
22 **to charge at s.o.:** jdn. angreifen.
24 **to impel:** zwingen, treiben.

door slammed violently and was locked. The chair and
bed seemed to be executing a dance of triumph for a moment, and then abruptly everything was still.

Mrs. Hall was left almost in a fainting condition in Mr.
5 Hall's arms on the landing. It was with the greatest difficulty that Mr. Hall and Millie, who had been roused by
her scream of alarm, succeeded in getting her downstairs, and applying the restoratives customary in these
cases.

10 "'Tas sperrits," said Mrs. Hall. "I know 'tas sperrits. I've
read in papers of en. Tables and chairs leaping and danc-
ing! —"

"Take a drop more, Janny," said Hall. "'Twill steady
ye."

15 "Lock him out," said Mrs. Hall. "Don't let him come in
again. I half guessed – I might ha' known. With them
goggling eyes and bandaged head, and never going to
church of a Sunday. And all they bottles – more'n it's
right for any one to have. He's put the sperrits into the
20 furniture – My good old furniture! 'Twas in that very
chair my poor dear mother used to sit when I was a little
girl. To think it should rise up against me now!"

"Just a drop more, Janny," said Hall. "Your nerves is all
upset."

25 They sent Millie across the street through the golden

---

4 **to faint:** ohnmächtig werden.
8 **restorative:** Stärkungsmittel.
   customary: üblich.
10 **'tas sperrits** (dial.): *it was spirits; there were spirits.*
11 **of en** (dial.): *of them.*
13 f. **'twill steady ye** (dial.): *it will steady you:* das wird dich beruhigen.
16 **ha'** (dial.): *have.*
18 f. **more'n it's right** (dial.): *more than is right.*

five o'clock sunshine to rouse up Mr. Sandy Wadgers,
the blacksmith. Mr. Hall's compliments and the furniture
upstairs was behaving most extraordinary. Would Mr.
Wadgers come round? He was a knowing man, was Mr.
5 Wadgers, and very resourceful. He took quite a grave
view of the case. "Arm darmed ef thet ent witchcraft,"
was the view of Mr. Sandy Wadgers. "You warnt horse-
shoes for such gentry as he."

He came round greatly concerned. They wanted him to
10 lead the way upstairs to the room, but he didn't seem to
be in any hurry. He preferred to talk in the passage. Over
the way Huxter's apprentice came out and began taking
down the shutters of the tobacco window. He was called
over to join the discussion. Mr. Huxter naturally fol-
15 lowed in the course of a few minutes. The Anglo-Saxon
genius for parliamentary government asserted itself;
there was a great deal of talk and no decisive action.
"Let's have the facts first," insisted Mr. Sandy Wadgers.
"Let's be sure we'd be acting perfectly right in bustin'
20 that there door open. A door onbust is always open to
bustin', but ye can't onbust a door once you've busted
en."

---

2 **blacksmith:** Schmied.
5 **resourceful:** findig.
6 **Arm darmed ef thet ent witchcraft** (dial.): *I'm damned if that isn't*
   witchcraft (*witchcraft:* Hexerei).
7 **warnt:** Want.
7f. **horseshoe:** Hufeisen.
8 **gentry** (slang): Pack, Leute.
12 **apprentice:** Lehrling.
16 **genius:** Talent, Begabung: hier auch: (fig.) Neigung.
19f. **to bust open:** (Tür) aufbrechen.
20 **that there door** (dial.): *that door there.*
   a door onbust (dial.): *an unbusted door.*

And suddenly and most wonderfully the door of the
room upstairs opened of its own accord, and as they
looked up in amazement, they saw descending the stairs
the muffled figure of the stranger staring more blackly
5 and blankly than ever with those unreasonably large
blue glass eyes of his. He came down stiffly and slowly,
staring all the time; he walked across the passage staring,
then stopped.

"Look there!" he said, and their eyes followed the direc-
10 tion of his gloved finger and saw a bottle of sarsaparilla
hard by the cellar door. Then he entered the parlour, and
suddenly, swiftly, viciously, slammed the door in their
faces.

Not a word was spoken until the last echoes of the slam
15 had died away. They stared at one another. "Well, if that
don't lick everything!" said Mr. Wadgers, and left the al-
ternative unsaid.

"I'd go in and ask'n 'bout it," said Wadgers, to Mr. Hall.
"I'd d'mand an explanation."
20 It took some time to bring the landlady's husband up to
that pitch. At last he rapped, opened the door, and got as
far as, "Excuse me —"

"Go to the devil!" said the stranger in a tremendous
voice, and "Shut that door after you." So that brief inter-
25 view terminated.

---

2 **of one's own accord:** von selbst, von allein.
12 **viciously** (adv.): boshaft.
15f. **if that don't lick everything** (infml.): das haut doch dem Faß den
Boden aus.
18 **ask'n** (dial.): *ask him.*
20 **landlady:** Hauswirtin.
20f. **to bring s.o. up to that pitch:** (fig.) jdn. so weit, dahin bringen (*pitch:*
Grad, Höhe, Maß).
25 **to terminate:** enden, beendigt sein.

Chapter VII

The Unveiling of the Stranger

The stranger went into the little parlour of the Coach
and Horses about half-past five in the morning, and
5 there he remained until near midday, the blinds down,
the door shut, and none, after Hall's repulse, venturing
near him.

All that time he must have fasted. Thrice he rang his
bell, the third time furiously and continuously, but no
10 one answered him. "Him and his 'go to the devil' indeed!" said Mrs. Hall. Presently came an imperfect rumour of the burglary at the vicarage, and two and two
were put together. Hall, assisted by Wadgers, went off to
find Mr. Shuckleforth, the magistrate, and take his ad-
15 vice. No one ventured upstairs. How the stranger occupied himself is unknown. Now and then he would stride
violently up and down, and twice came an outburst of
curses, a tearing of paper, and a violent smashing of bottles.

20 The little group of scared but curious people increased.
Mrs. Huxter came over; some gay young fellows resplendent in black ready-made jackets and *piqué* paper ties,

---

2 **unveiling:** Enthüllung.
6 **repulse:** Abfuhr, Zurückweisung.
11 f. **rumour:** Gerücht.
14 **magistrate:** Friedensrichter.
18 **to smash:** zerschmettern.
21 f. **resplendent:** herausgeputzt.
22 **ready-made jacket:** Konfektionsjacke.
  piqué (Fr.): hier: mit plastischen Oberflächenmusterungen versehen
  (von frz. *piqué* ›Pikee, Baumwollstoff mit Reliefmuster‹).

for it was Whit-Monday, joined the group with confused
interrogations. Young Archie Harker distinguished himself by going up the yard and trying to peep under the
window-blinds. He could see nothing, but gave reason
5 for supposing that he did, and others of the Iping youth
presently joined him.

It was the finest of all possible Whit-Mondays, and down
the village street stood a row of nearly a dozen booths
and a shooting gallery, and on the grass by the forge
10 were three yellow and chocolate waggons and some pic-
turesque strangers of both sexes putting up a cocoanut
shy. The gentlemen wore blue jerseys, the ladies white
aprons and quite fashionable hats with heavy plumes.
Wodger of the Purple Fawn and Mr. Jaggers the cobbler,
15 who also sold second-hand ordinary bicycles, were
stretching a string of union-jacks and royal ensigns
(which had originally celebrated the Jubilee) across the
road ...

And inside, in the artificial darkness of the parlour, in-
20 to which only one thin jet of sunlight penetrated, the

2f. **to distinguish o.s.:** sich auszeichnen, hervortun.
8 **booth:** Jahrmarktsbude.
9 **shooting gallery:** Schießbude.
11f. **cocoanut shy:** Kokosnußwerfen.
12 **jersey:** Pullover.
13 **apron:** Schürze.
    plume: (Hut-)Feder.
14 **the Purple Fawn:** Name eines Gasthauses (*purple:* dunkelrot; *fawn:* Kitz).
    cobbler: Schuster.
16 **union-jack:** britische Nationalflagge.
    royal ensign: königliche Flagge.
17 **Jubilee:** gemeint ist das Thronjubiläum Königin Victorias (1819 bis 1901).
20 **to penetrate:** durchdringen.

stranger, hungry we must suppose, and fearful, hidden
in his uncomfortable hot wrappings, pored through his
dark glasses upon his paper or chinked his dirty little bottles, and occasionally swore savagely at the boys, audible
5 if invisible, outside the windows. In the corner by the fireplace lay the fragments of half a dozen smashed bottles,
and a pungent tang of chlorine tainted the air. So much we
know from what was heard at the time and from what was
subsequently seen in the room.

10 About noon he suddenly opened his parlour door and
stood glaring fixedly at the three or four people in the
bar. "Mrs. Hall," he said. Somebody went sheepishly
and called for Mrs. Hall.

Mrs. Hall appeared after an interval, a little short of
15 breath, but all the fiercer for that. Hall was still out. She
had deliberated over this scene, and she came holding a
little tray with an unsettled bill upon it. "Is it your bill
you're wanting, sir?" she said.

"Why wasn't my breakfast laid? Why haven't you pre-
20 pared my meals and answered my bell? Do you think I
live without eating?"

"Why isn't my bill paid?" said Mrs. Hall. "That's what I
want to know."

---

2 **wrapping:** Verpackung, Umhüllung.
2f. **to pore upon s.th.:** über einer Sache brüten.
3 **to chink s.th.:** mit etwas klirren.
7 **pungent:** (fig.) beißend.
   tang: Geruch.
   chlorine: Chlor.
   to taint: durchtränken.
9 **subsequently** (adv.): hinterher, später.
12 **sheepishly** (adv.): verlegen.
16 **to deliberate:** sorgfältig nachdenken.

"I told you three days ago I was awaiting a remittance —"

"I told you two days ago I wasn't going to await no remittances. You can't grumble if your breakfast waits a bit, if
5 my bill's been waiting these five days, can you?"

The stranger swore briefly but vividly.

"Nar, nar!" from the bar.

"And I'd thank you kindly, sir, if you'd keep your swearing to yourself, sir," said Mrs. Hall.

10 The stranger stood looking more like an angry diving-helmet than ever. It was universally felt in the bar that Mrs. Hall had the better of him. His next words showed as much.

"Look here, my good woman –" he began.

15 "Don't good woman *me*," said Mrs. Hall.

"I've told you my remittance hasn't come —"

"Remittance indeed!" said Mrs. Hall.

"Still, I daresay in my pocket —"

"You told me two days ago that you hadn't anything but
20 a sovereign's worth of silver upon you —"

"Well, I've found some more —"

"'Ul-*lo*" from the bar.

"I wonder where you found it!" said Mrs. Hall.

That seemed to annoy the stranger very much. He
25 stamped his foot. "What do you mean?" he said.

---

1 f. **remittance:** Überweisung.
4 **to grumble:** sich beklagen, murren.
7 **nar, nar!:** na, na!
11 **universally** (adv.): allgemein.
12 **to have the better of s.o.:** die Oberhand über jdn. behalten.
15 **don't good woman me:** ich bin nicht Ihre gute Frau.
18 **I daresay:** ich glaube wohl.
22 **'ullo** (dial.): *hullo.*

"That I wonder where you found it," said Mrs. Hall.
"And before I take any bills or get any breakfasts, or do
any such things whatsoever, you got to tell me one or two
things I don't understand, and what nobody don't under-
5 stand, and what everybody is very anxious to understand. I want know what you been doing t' my chair upstairs, and I want know how 'tis your room was empty,
and how you got in again. Them as stops in this house
comes in by the doors, – that's the rule of the house, and
10 that you *didn't* do, and what I want know is how you *did*
come in. And I want know —"
Suddenly the stranger raised his gloved hands clenched,
stamped his foot, and said, "Stop!" with such extraordinary violence that he silenced her instantly.
15 "You don't understand," he said, "who I am or what I
am. I'll show you. By Heaven! I'll show you." Then he
put his open palm over his face and withdrew it. The centre of his face became a black cavity. "Here," he said. He
stepped forward and handed Mrs. Hall something which
20 she, staring at his metamorphosed face, accepted auto-
matically. Then, when she saw what it was, she screamed
loudly, dropped it, and staggered back. The nose – it was
the stranger's nose! pink and shining – rolled on the
floor.
25 Then he removed his spectacles, and every one in the
bar gasped. He took off his hat, and with a violent ges-

---

6 **I want know** (dial.): *I want to know.*
8f. **Them as stops in this house comes in** (dial.): *Those who stop in this
house come in.*
12 **to clench:** zusammenpressen, ballen.
17 **palm:** Handfläche.
18 **cavity:** Höhlung.
20 **metamorphosed:** verwandelt.

ture tore at his whiskers and bandages. For a moment
they resisted him. A flash of horrible anticipation passed
through the bar. "Oh, my Gard!" said some one. Then
off they came.

5 It was worse than anything. Mrs. Hall, standing open-
mouthed and horror-struck, shrieked at what she saw,
and made for the door of the house. Every one began to
move. They were prepared for scars, disfigurements,
tangible horrors, but *nothing!* The bandages and false
hair flew across the passage into the bar, making a hobbledehoy jump to avoid them. Every one tumbled on
every one else down the steps. For the man who stood
there shouting some incoherent explanation, was a solid
gesticulating figure up to the coat-collar of him, and then
– nothingness, no visible thing at all!

People down the village heard shouts and shrieks, and
looking up the street saw the Coach and Horses violently firing out its humanity. They saw Mrs. Hall fall
down and Mr. Teddy Henfrey jump to avoid tumbling
over her, and then they heard the frightful screams of
Millie, who, emerging suddenly from the kitchen at the
noise of the tumult, had come upon the headless
stranger from behind.

---

2 **anticipation:** Ahnung.
3 **my Gard** (dial.): *my God.*
8 **scar:** Narbe.
   disfigurement: Entstellung.
9 **tangible:** greifbar.
10f. **hobbledehoy** (arch.): Tolpatsch; hier: tolpatschig, ungeschickt.
13 **incoherent:** unzusammenhängend.
18 **to fire s.th. out:** (fig.) etwas ausspucken.
   humanity: gemeint sind die Menschen im Gasthaus.
21 **to emerge:** auftauchen.

Forthwith every one all down the street, the sweetstuff
seller, cocoanut shy proprietor and his assistant, the
swing man, little boys and girls, rustic dandies, smart
wenches, smocked elders and aproned gipsies, began
5 running towards the inn; and in a miraculously short
space of time a crowd of perhaps forty people, and rapidly increasing, swayed and hooted and inquired and exclaimed and suggested, in front of Mrs. Hall's establish-
ment. Every one seemed eager to talk at once, and the
10 result was babel. A small group supported Mrs. Hall,
who was picked up in a state of collapse. There was a
conference, and the incredible evidence of a vociferous
eye-witness. "O' Bogey!" "What's he been doin', then?"
"Ain't hurt the girl, 'as 'e?" "Run at en with a knife, I be-
15 lieve." "No 'ed, I tell ye. I don't mean no manner of
speaking, I mean *marn 'ithout a 'ed!*" "Narnsense! 'tas

---

1 **forthwith** (adv., fml.): sofort, unverzüglich.
3 **swing man:** Schiffschaukelbesitzer.
  rustic dandies: feiertäglich gekleidete Burschen vom Lande.
4 **wench** (arch.): Landmädchen.
  smocked elders: herausgeputzte ältere Frauen (*smock:* Überkleid
  aus weißem Leinen).
  gipsy: Zigeuner(in).
7 **to sway:** wogen, schwanken.
  to hoot: schreien, johlen.
10 **babel:** unverständliches Stimmengewirr.
12 **vociferous:** laut, wortreich.
13 **o' Bogey!:** o Gott!
14 **'as 'e?** (dial.): *has he?*
  en (dial.): *her.*
15 **no 'ed** (dial.): *no head.*
15f. **I don't mean no manner of speaking:** das ist nicht nur so eine Re-
  densart.
16 **narnsense** (dial.): *nonsense.*

some conjuring trick." "Fetched off 'is wrappin's, 'e did —"

In its struggles to see in through the open door, the crowd formed itself into a straggling wedge, with the more adventurous apex nearest the inn. "He stood for a moment, I heerd the gal scream, and he turned. I saw her skirts whisk, and he went after her. Didn't take ten seconds. Back he comes with a knife in uz hand and a loaf; stood just as if he was staring. Not a moment ago. Went in that there door. I tell 'e, 'e ain't gart no 'ed 't all. You just missed en —"

There was a disturbance behind, and the speaker stopped to step aside for a little procession that was marching very resolutely towards the house, – first Mr. Hall, very red and determined, then Mr. Bobby Jaffers, the village constable, and then the wary Mr. Wadgers. They had come now armed with a warrant.

People shouted conflicting information of the recent circumstances. "'Ed or no 'ed," said Jaffers, "I got to 'rest en, and 'rest en I *will*."

---

1 **conjuring trick:** Zauberkunststück.
   to fetch off: (Kleider) abwerfen.
4 **straggling:** weit verteilt.
   wedge: Keil.
5 **apex:** Spitze.
6 **I heerd the gal scream** (dial.): *I heard the girl scream.*
10 **I tell 'e, 'e ain't gart no 'ed 't all** (dial.): *I tell you, he hasn't got a head at all.*
12 **disturbance:** Bewegung, Unruhe, Aufruhr.
16 **village constable:** Dorfpolizist.
   wary: vorsichtig, auf der Hut.
17 **warrant:** Haftbefehl.
18 **conflicting:** widersprüchlich.
19f. **I got to 'rest en** (dial.): *I've got to arrest him.*

Mr. Hall marched up the steps, marched straight to the door of the parlour and flung it open. "Constable," he said, "do your duty."

Jaffers marched in, Hall next, Wadgers last. They saw in
5 the dim light the headless figure facing them, with a gnawed crust of bread in one gloved hand and a chunk of cheese in the other.

"That's him!" said Hall.

"What the devil's this?" came in a tone of angry ex-
10 postulation from above the collar of the figure.

"You're a damned rum customer, mister," said Mr. Jaffers. "But 'ed or no 'ed, the warrant says 'body,' and duty's duty —"

"Keep off!" said the figure, starting back.

15 Abruptly he whipped down the bread and cheese, and Mr. Hall just grasped the knife on the table in time to save it. Off came the stranger's left glove and was slapped in Jaffers' face. In another moment Jaffers, cutting short some statement concerning a warrant, had
20 gripped him by the handless wrist and caught his invisible throat. He got a sounding kick on the shin that made him shout, but he kept his grip. Hall sent the knife sliding along the table to Wadgers, who acted as goal-keeper for the offensive, so to speak, and then stepped forward
25 as Jaffers and the stranger swayed and staggered towards him, clutching and hitting in. A chair stood in the

---

6 **to gnaw:** (an-, zer)nagen.
   chunk: großes Stück, Brocken.
9 f. **expostulation:** Protest.
18 **to slap:** schlagen.
21 **sounding:** heftig.
   shin: Schienbein.

way, and went aside with a crash as they came down together.

"Get the feet," said Jaffers between his teeth. Mr. Hall, endeavouring to act on instructions, received a sounding kick in the ribs that disposed of him for a moment, and Mr. Wadgers, seeing the decapitated stranger had rolled over and got the upper side of Jaffers, retreated towards the door, knife in hand, and so collided with Mr. Huxter and the Siddermorton carter coming to the rescue of law and order. At the same moment down came three or four bottles from the chiffonnier and shot a web of pungency into the air of the room.

"I'll surrender," cried the stranger, though he had Jaffers down, and in another moment he stood up panting, a strange figure, headless and handless, – for he had pulled off his right glove now as well as his left. "It's no good," he said, as if sobbing for breath.

It was the strangest thing in the world to hear that voice coming as if out of empty space, but the Sussex peasants are perhaps the most matter-of-fact people under the sun. Jaffers got up also and produced a pair of handcuffs. Then he started.

4 **to endeavour:** sich bemühen.
5 **to dispose of s.o.:** jdn. kampfunfähig machen.
6 **decapitated:** ohne Kopf.
8 **to collide:** zusammenstoßen, -prallen.
9 **carter:** Fuhrmann.
12 **to shoot a web of pungency into the air** (fig.): einen stechenden Geruch verbreiten (*web:* Gewebe, Gespinst).
14 **to pant:** keuchen.
17 **to sob for breath:** nach Atem ringen.
20 **matter-of-fact:** nüchtern.
21 **handcuffs:** Handschellen.

"I say!" said Jaffers, brought up short by a dim realisation of the incongruity of the whole business, "Darm it!
Can't use 'em as I can see."

The stranger ran his arm down his waistcoat, and as if by
5 a miracle the buttons to which his empty sleeve pointed
became undone. Then he said something about his shin,
and stooped down. He seemed to be fumbling with his
shoes and socks.

"Why!" said Huxter, suddenly, "that's not a man at all.
10 It's just empty clothes. Look! You can see down his collar and the linings of his clothes. I could put my
arm —"

He extended his hand; it seemed to meet something in
mid-air, and he drew it back with a sharp exclamation. "I
15 wish you'd keep your fingers out of my eye," said the
aerial voice, in a tone of savage expostulation. "The fact
is, I'm all here: head, hands, legs, and all the rest of it, but
it happens I'm invisible. It's a confounded nuisance, but
I am. That's no reason why I should be poked to pieces
20 by every stupid bumpkin in Iping, is it?"

The suit of clothes, now all unbuttoned and hanging

---

1 **brought up short:** plötzlich innehaltend.
1 f. **dim realisation:** schwache, unklare Vorstellung.
2 **incongruity:** Ungereimtheit, Widersinn.
  darm it! (dial.): *damn it.*
4 **waistcoat:** Weste.
6 **undone:** offen (Knöpfe).
11 **lining:** Futter(stoff).
13 f. **in mid-air:** mitten in der Luft.
16 **aerial:** aus der Luft kommend.
18 **confounded nuisance:** verdammtes, verflixtes Ärgernis.
19 **to poke:** stoßen, hauen.
20 **bumpkin:** Bauerntölpel.

loosely upon its unseen supports, stood up, arms akimbo.

Several other of the men folks had now entered the room, so that it was closely crowded. "Invisible, eigh?" said Huxter, ignoring the stranger's abuse. "Who ever heard the likes of that?"

"It's strange, perhaps, but it's not a crime. Why am I assaulted by a policeman in this fashion?"

"Ah! that's a different matter," said Jaffers. "No doubt you are a bit difficult to see in this light, but I got a warrant and it's all correct. What I'm after ain't no invisibility, – it's burglary. There's a house been broken into and money took."

"Well?"

"And circumstances certainly point —"

"Stuff and nonsense!" said the Invisible Man.

"I hope so, sir; but I've got my instructions."

"Well," said the stranger, "I'll come. I'll *come*. But no handcuffs."

"It's the regular thing," said Jaffers.

"No handcuffs," stipulated the stranger.

"Pardon me," said Jaffers.

Abruptly the figure sat down, and before any one could realise what was being done, the slippers, socks, and trousers had been kicked off under the table. Then he sprang up again and flung off his coat.

"Here, stop that," said Jaffers, suddenly realising what was happening. He gripped the waistcoat; it struggled,

---

1 f. **arms akimbo:** die Arme in die Seiten gestemmt.

5 **abuse:** zornige Sprache, Schimpfen.

6 **the likes of that:** derartiges.

7 f. **to assault:** angreifen.

21 **to stipulate:** fordern, zur Bedingung machen.

and the shirt slipped out of it and left it limp and empty
in his hand. "Hold him!" said Jaffers, loudly. "Once he
gets they things off —!"

"Hold him!" cried every one, and there was a rush at the
5 fluttering white shirt which was now all that was visible
of the stranger.

The shirt-sleeve planted a shrewd blow in Hall's face
that stopped his open-armed advance, and sent him
backward into old Toothsome the sexton, and in another
10 moment the garment was lifted up and became con-
vulsed and vacantly flapping about the arms, even as a
shirt that is being thrust over a man's head. Jaffers
clutched at it, and only helped to pull it off; he was struck
in the mouth out of the air, and incontinently drew his
15 truncheon and smote Teddy Henfrey savagely upon the
crown of his head.

"Look out!" said everybody, fencing at random and hitting at nothing. "Hold him! Shut the door! Don't let him
loose! I got something! Here he is!" A perfect babel of
20 noises they made. Everybody, it seemed, was being hit
all at once, and Sandy Wadgers, knowing as ever and his
wits sharpened by a frightful blow in the nose, reopened

---

1 **limp:** schlaff.
7 **shrewd:** hier: wohlgezielt.
9 **sexton:** Küster, Kirchendiener.
10 f. **to convulse:** in Zuckungen versetzen, schütteln.
11 **vacantly** (adv.): leer.
   to flap: flattern.
14 **incontinently** (adv., arch.): sofort, unverzüglich, ohne sich zu besinnen.
15 **truncheon:** Knüppel.
   smote: Prät. von *to smite:* schlagen.
16 **crown:** Scheitel.
17 **at random:** aufs Geratewohl.

the door and led the rout. The others, following incontinently, were jammed for a moment in the corner by the
doorway. The hitting continued. Phipps, the Unitarian,
had a front tooth broken, and Henfrey was injured in the
cartilage of his ear. Jaffers was struck under the jaw, and,
turning, caught at something that intervened between
him and Huxter in the *mêlée*, and prevented their coming together. He felt a muscular chest, and in another
moment the whole mass of struggling, excited men shot
out into the crowded hall.

"I got him!" shouted Jaffers, choking and reeling
through them all, and wrestling with purple face and
swelling veins against his unseen enemy.

Men staggered right and left as the extraordinary con-
flict swayed swiftly towards the house door, and went
spinning down the half-dozen steps of the inn. Jaffers
cried in a strangled voice, – holding tight, nevertheless,
and making play with his knee, – spun round, and fell
heavily undermost with his head on the gravel. Only
then did his fingers relax.

---

1 **rout:** Flucht.
2 **to be jammed:** eingekeilt sein.
3 **Unitarian:** Unitarier (Gegner des Dogmas von der Dreifaltigkeit
 Gottes).
5 **cartilage:** Knorpel.
6 **to intervene:** dazwischentreten, sich in den Weg stellen.
7 **mêlée** (Fr.): Handgemenge, Getümmel.
11 **to choke:** röcheln.
 to reel: schwanken, taumeln.
12 **to wrestle:** ringen, kämpfen.
16 **to spin:** (sich) drehen.
17 **in a strangled voice:** mit erstickter Stimme.
18 **to make play:** zur Geltung bringen.
19 **undermost** (adv.): zuunterst.
 gravel: Kies.

There were excited cries of "Hold him!" "Invisible!" and
so forth, and a young fellow, a stranger in the place whose
name did not come to light, rushed in at once, caught
something, missed his hold, and fell over the constable's
5 prostrate body. Halfway across the road a woman
screamed as something pushed by her; a dog, kicked apparently, yelped and ran howling into Huxter's yard, and
with that the transit of the Invisible Man was accom-
plished. For a space people stood amazed and gesticulat-
10 ing, and then came Panic, and scattered them abroad
through the village as a gust scatters dead leaves.
But Jaffers lay quite still, face upward and knees bent.

Chapter VIII

In Transit

15 The eighth chapter is exceedingly brief, and relates that
Gibbins, the amateur naturalist of the district, while lying out on the spacious open downs without a soul
within a couple of miles of him, as he thought, and almost dozing, heard close to him the sound as of a man
20 coughing, sneezing, and then swearing savagely to him-

---

5 **prostrate:** am Boden liegend.
8 **transit:** hier: Flucht.
9 **for a space:** eine Zeitlang.
11 **gust:** Bö, Windstoß.
15 **exceedingly** (adv.): außerordentlich.
16 **naturalist:** Naturforscher.
17 **spacious:** weiträumig.

self; and looking, beheld nothing. Yet the voice was indisputable. It continued to swear with that breadth and variety that distinguishes the swearing of a cultivated man. It grew to a climax, diminished again, and died away in the distance, going as it seemed to him in the direction of Adderdean. It lifted to a spasmodic sneeze and ended. Gibbins had heard nothing of the morning's occurrences, but the phenomenon was so striking and disturbing that his philosophical tranquillity vanished; he got up hastily, and hurried down the steepness of the hill towards the village, as fast as he could go.

Chapter IX

Mr. Thomas Marvel

You must picture Mr. Thomas Marvel as a person of copious, flexible visage, a nose of cylindrical protrusion, a liquorish, ample, fluctuating mouth, and a beard of bristling eccentricity. His figure inclined to embonpoint; his

---

1 **to behold** (poet.): erblicken.
1 f. **to be indisputable:** hier: unbestreitbar vorhanden sein.
4 **climax:** Höhepunkt.
9 **tranquillity:** Ruhe.
14 f. **copious:** breit, massig.
15 **protrusion:** Vorstehen, Vorspringen.
16 **liquorish:** an Alkohol gewöhnt (von *liquor* ›Alkohol, Spirituosen‹).
 ample: breit.
 fluctuating mouth: Triefmaul.
16 f. **of bristling eccentricity:** von ungeheuerer Struppigkeit.
17 **embonpoint** (Fr.): Wohlbeleibtheit.

short limbs accentuated this inclination. He wore a furry
silk hat, and the frequent substitution of twine and shoe-
laces for buttons, apparent at critical points of his costume, marked a man essentially bachelor.

5 Mr. Thomas Marvel was sitting with his feet in a ditch by
the roadside over the down towards Adderdean, about a
mile and a half out of Iping. His feet, save for socks of irregular open-work, were bare, his big toes were broad,
and pricked like the ears of a watchful dog. In a leisurely

10 manner – he did everything in a leisurely manner – he
was contemplating trying on a pair of boots. They were
the soundest boots he had come across for a long time,
but too large for him; whereas the ones he had were, in
dry weather, a very comfortable fit, but too thin-soled

15 for damp. Mr. Thomas Marvel hated roomy boots, but
then he hated damp. He had never properly thought out
which he hated most, and it was a pleasant day, and there
was nothing better to do. So he put the four boots in a
graceful group on the turf and looked at them. And see-

20 ing them there among the grass and springing agrimony,

---

1 **furry:** pelzig, haarig, flauschig; hier vermutl.: abgenutzt.
2 **silk hat:** Zylinder.
   substitution: Ersetzen, Austausch.
   twine: Bindfaden, Schnur.
2f. **shoe-laces** (pl.): Schnürsenkel.
4 **bachelor:** Junggeselle.
7f. **socks of irregular open-work:** zerrissene Socken.
9 **to prick:** hochstehen, nach oben gerichtet sein.
10 **leisurely:** gemächlich, gemütlich.
14 **to be a comfortable fit:** angenehm passend sein, bequem passen.
19 **graceful:** zierlich.
   turf: Rasen, Gras.
20 **to spring:** (empor)sprießen.
   agrimony: Leberblümchen (wildwachsende Frühlingsblume).

it suddenly occurred to him that both pairs were exceedingly ugly to see. He was not at all startled by a voice behind him.

"They're boots, anyhow," said the Voice.

"They are – charity boots," said Mr. Thomas Marvel, with his head on one side regarding them distastefully; "and which is the ugliest pair in the whole blessed universe, I'm darned if I know!"

"H'm," said the Voice.

"I've worn worse, – in fact, I've worn none. But none so owdacious ugly, – if you'll allow the expression. I've been cadging boots – in particular – for days. Because I was sick of *them*. They're sound enough, of course. But a gentleman on tramp sees such a thundering lot of his boots. And if you'll believe me, I've raised nothing in the whole blessed county, try as I would, but THEM. Look at 'em! And a good county for boots, too, in a general way. But it's just my promiscuous luck. I've got my boots in this county ten years or more. And then they treat you like this."

"It's a beast of a county," said the Voice. "And pigs for people."

"Ain't it?" said Mr. Thomas Marvel. "Lord! But them boots! It beats it."

---

5 **charity boots:** Wohltätigkeitsstiefel, d. h. geschenkte Stiefel.
8 **I'm darned if I know:** ich will verdammt sein, wenn ich es weiß.
11 **owdacious** (dial.): *audaciously* (adv.): unverfroren.
12 **to cadge** (infml.): betteln, schnorren.
14 **tramp:** Wanderung, Wanderschaft.
   thundering (infml.): gewaltig, unheimlich.
16 **blessed** (infml.): verflixt.
18 **promiscuous** (poet.): wechselhaft, launenhaft.
24 **it beats it** (infml.): das ist doch die Höhe (*to beat:* übertreffen).

He turned his head over his shoulder to the right, to look
at the boots of his interlocutor with a view to compari-
sons, and lo! where the boots of his interlocutor should
have been were neither legs nor boots. He turned his
head over his shoulder to the left, and there also were
neither legs nor boots. He was irradiated by the dawn of
a great amazement. "Where *are* yer?" said Mr. Thomas
Marvel over his shoulder and coming round on all fours.
He saw a stretch of empty downs with the wind swaying
the remote green-pointed furze bushes.

"Am I drunk?" said Mr. Marvel. "Have I had visions?
Was I talking to myself? What the —"

"Don't be alarmed," said a Voice.

"None of your ventriloquising *me*," said Mr. Thomas
Marvel, rising sharply to his feet. "Where *are* yer?
Alarmed, indeed!"

"Don't be alarmed," repeated the Voice.

"*You'll* be alarmed in a minute, you silly fool," said Mr.
Thomas Marvel. "Where *are* yer? Lemme get my mark
on yer —

Are you *buried?*" said Mr. Thomas Marvel, after an
interval.

There was no answer. Mr. Thomas Marvel stood boot-
less and amazed, his jacket nearly thrown off.

---

2 **interlocutor:** Gesprächspartner.
3 **lo!** (poet.): siehe, seht da!
6 **to irradiate** (poet.): erhellen.
10 **remote:** entfernt (liegend).
    furze: Ginster.
14 **to ventriloquise s.o.:** zu jdm. bauchreden.
19 **lemme** (dial.): *let me.*
19f. **to get one's mark on s.th.:** sich eine Vorstellung, einen Begriff von
    etwas machen.

"Peewit," said a peewit, very remote.

"Peewit, indeed!" said Mr. Thomas Marvel. "This ain't no time for foolery." The down was desolate, east and west, north and south; the road, with its shallow ditches and white bordering stakes, ran smooth and empty north and south, and, save for that peewit, the blue sky was empty too. "So help me," said Mr. Thomas Marvel, shuffling his coat on to his shoulders again. "It's the drink! I might ha' known."

"It's not the drink," said the Voice. "You keep your nerves steady."

"Ow!" said Mr. Marvel, and his face grew white amidst its patches. "It's the drink," his lips repeated noiselessly. He remained staring about him, rotating slowly backwards. "I could have *swore* I heard a voice," he whispered.

"Of course you did."

"It's there again," said Mr. Marvel, closing his eyes and clasping his hand on his brow with a tragic gesture. He was suddenly taken by the collar and shaken violently, and left more dazed than ever. "Don't be a fool," said the Voice.

"I'm – off – my – blooming – chump," said Mr. Marvel.

---

1 **peewit:** Kiebitz.
3 **desolate:** wie ausgestorben.
4 **shallow:** flach, seicht.
5 **bordering stakes** (pl.): Grenzpfosten.
7 f. **to shuffle:** schieben, ziehen.
15 **swore** (dial.): *sworn.*
21 **dazed:** benommen, betäubt.
23 **I'm off my blooming chump** (slang): ich hab meinen verfluchten Verstand verloren (*blooming* [slang]: verflixt, verflucht).

"It's no good. It's fretting about them blarsted boots. I'm off my blessed blooming chump. Or it's spirits."

"Neither one thing nor the other," said the Voice. "Listen!"

5 "Chump," said Mr. Marvel.

"One minute," said the Voice penetratingly, – tremulous with self-control.

"Well?" said Mr. Thomas Marvel, with a strange feeling of having been dug in the chest by a finger.

10 "You think I'm just imagination? Just imagination?"

"What else *can* you be?" said Mr. Thomas Marvel, rubbing the back of his neck.

"Very well," said the Voice, in a tone of relief. "Then I'm going to throw flints at you till you think differently."

15 "But where *are* yer?"

The Voice made no answer. Whizz came a flint, apparently out of the air, and missed Mr. Marvel's shoulder by a hair's breadth. Mr. Marvel, turning, saw a flint jerk up into the air, trace a complicated path, hang for a mo-
20 ment, and then fling at his feet with almost invisible rapidity. He was too amazed to dodge. Whizz it came, and ricochetted from a bare toe into the ditch. Mr. Thomas Marvel jumped a foot and howled aloud. Then he started to run, tripped over an unseen obstacle, and
25 came head over heels into a sitting position.

---

1 **them blarsted boots** (dial.): *those blasted boots* (vulg.): diese verdammten Stiefel.
14 **flint:** Kieselstein.
16 **whizz:** sausendes Geräusch.
18 **to jerk up:** in die Höhe schnellen.
21 **to dodge:** ausweichen.
22 **to ricochet:** abprallen.
25 **head over heels:** kopfüber.

"*Now*," said the Voice, as a third stone curved upward and hung in the air above the tramp. "Am I imagination?"

Mr. Marvel by way of reply struggled to his feet, and was immediately rolled over again. He lay quiet for a moment. "If you struggle any more," said the Voice, "I shall throw the flint at your head."

"It's a fair do," said Mr. Thomas Marvel, sitting up, taking his wounded toe in hand and fixing his eye on the third missile. "I don't understand it. Stones flinging themselves. Stones talking. Put yourself down. Rot away. I'm done."

The third flint fell.

"It's very simple," said the Voice. "I'm an invisible man."

"Tell us something I don't know," said Mr. Marvel, gasping with pain. "Where you've hid – how you do it – I *don't* know, I'm beat."

"That's all," said the Voice. "I'm invisible. That's what I want you to understand."

"Any one could see that. There is no need for you to be so confounded impatient, mister. *Now* then. Give us a notion. How are you hid?"

"I'm invisible. That's the great point. And what I want you to understand is this —"

"But whereabouts?" interrupted Mr. Marvel.

---

 1 **to curve:** einen (Kreis-)Bogen beschreiben, machen.
 2 **tramp:** Landstreicher.
 8 **it's a fair do:** ich geb mich geschlagen.
10 **missile:** Wurfgeschoß.
11f. **rot away** (vulg.): hol euch der Teufel.
17f. **hid / beat** (dial.): *hidden, beaten*.
26 **But whereabouts?:** Aber wo sind Sie denn? (*whereabouts* [pl.]: Aufenthalt).

"Here! Six yards in front of you."

"Oh, *come!* I ain't blind. You'll be telling me next you're just thin air. I'm not one of your ignorant tramps —"

5 "Yes, I am – thin air. You're looking through me."

"What! Ain't there any stuff to you? *Vox et* – what is it? – jabber. Is it that?"

"I am just a human being – solid, needing food and drink, needing covering too – But I'm invisible. You see?
10 Invisible. Simple idea. Invisible."

"What, real like?"

"Yes, real."

"Let's have a hand of you," said Marvel, "if you *are* real. It won't be so darn out-of-the-way like, then –
15 *Lord!*" he said, "how you made me jump! – gripping me like that!"

He felt the hand that had closed round his wrist with his disengaged fingers, and his touch went timorously up the arm, patted a muscular chest, and explored a bearded
20 face. Marvel's face was astonishment.

"I'm dashed!" he said. "If this don't beat cock-fighting! Most remarkable! – And there I can see a rabbit clean through you, 'arf a mile away! Not a bit of you visible – except —"

---

6 **vox et** (Lat.): *vox et praeterea nihil:* eine Stimme und nichts mehr, Worte nichts als Worte.

7 **jabber:** Geschnatter, Geplapper.

14 **darn** (slang): *damn.*

18 **disengaged:** frei.
  timorously (adv.): schüchtern, zaghaft.

21 **I'm dashed** (infml.): ich bin ‚platt'.
  If this don't beat cock-fighting! (infml.): Das übertrifft sogar Hahnenkämpfe (damals waren Hahnenkämpfe in England sehr populär).

23 **'arf** (dial.): *half.*

He scrutinised the apparently empty space keenly. "You 'aven't been eatin' bread and cheese?" he asked, holding the invisible arm.

"You're quite right, and it's not quite assimilated into the system."

"Ah!" said Mr. Marvel. "Sort of ghostly, though."

"Of course, all this isn't half so wonderful as you think."

"It's quite wonderful enough for *my* modest wants," said Mr. Thomas Marvel. "Howjer manage it! How the dooce is it done?"

"It's too long a story. And besides —"

"I tell you, the whole business fair beats me," said Mr. Marvel.

"What I want to say at present is this: I need help. I have come to that – I came upon you suddenly. I was wandering, mad with rage, naked, impotent. I could have murdered. And I saw you —"

"*Lord!*" said Mr. Marvel.

"I came up behind you – hesitated – went on —"

Mr. Marvel's expression was eloquent.

"– then stopped. 'Here,' I said, 'is an outcast like myself. This is the man for me.' So I turned back and came to you – you. And —"

"*Lord!*" said Mr. Marvel. "But I'm all in a dizzy. May I

---

4 **to assimilate:** aufnehmen.
6 **though** (infml.): aber, trotzdem.
10 **Howjer manage it** (dial.): *How do you manage it.*
    how the dooce (dial.): *how the deuce:* wie zum Teufel.
13 **fair** (adv., infml.): glatt, völlig.
17 **impotent:** schwach, hilflos.
22 **outcast:** Ausgestoßener.
25 **I'm all in a dizzy** (infml.): ich bin ganz verwirrt.

ask – How is it? And what you may be requiring in the
way of help? – Invisible!"

"I want you to help me get clothes – and shelter – and
then, with other things. I've left them long enough. If
5 you won't – well! But you *will* – *must*."

"Look here," said Mr. Marvel. "I'm too flabbergasted.
Don't knock me about any more. And leave me go. I
must get steady a bit. And you've pretty near broken my
toe. It's all so unreasonable. Empty downs, empty sky.
10 Nothing visible for miles except the bosom of Nature.
And then comes a voice. A voice out of heaven! And
stones! And a fist – Lord!"

"Pull yourself together," said the Voice, "for you have to
do the job I've chosen for you."

15 Mr. Marvel blew out his cheeks, and his eyes were
round.

"I've chosen you," said the Voice. "You are the only man
except some of those fools down there, who knows there
is such a thing as an invisible man. You have to be my
20 helper. Help me – and I will do great things for you. An
invisible man is a man of power." He stopped for a moment to sneeze violently.

"But if you betray me," he said, "if you fail to do as I di-
rect you —"

25 He paused and tapped Mr. Marvel's shoulder smartly.
Mr. Marvel gave a yelp of terror at the touch. "*I* don't
want to betray you," said Mr. Marvel, edging away from
the direction of the fingers. "Don't you go a-thinking

---

6 **to be flabbergasted** (infml.): verblüfft, ‚platt' sein.
25 **smartly** (adv.): schmerzhaft.
26 **yelp:** Heulen, Aufschrei.
27 **to edge away:** sich entziehen.
28 f. **don't you go a-thinking that** (dial.): glauben Sie nur das nicht.

that, whatever you do. All I want to do is to help you –
just tell me what I got to do. (Lord!) Whatever you want
done, that I'm most willing to do."

Chapter X

Mr. Marvel's Visit to Iping

6 After the first gusty panic had spent itself Iping became
argumentative. Scepticism suddenly reared its head, –
rather nervous scepticism, not at all assured of its back,
but scepticism nevertheless. It is so much easier not to
0 believe in an invisible man; and those who had actually
seen him dissolve into air, or felt the strength of his arm,
could be counted on the fingers of two hands. And of
these witnesses Mr. Wadgers was presently missing, having retired impregnably behind the bolts and bars of his
5 own house, and Jaffers was lying stunned in the parlour
of the Coach and Horses. Great and strange ideas tran-
scending experience often have less effect upon men and
women than smaller, more tangible considerations. Iping was gay with bunting, and everybody was in gala

---

6 **gusty:** (fig.) stürmisch, heftig.
7 **argumentative:** kritisch, zum Meinungsaustausch neigend.
11 **to dissolve:** sich auflösen.
14 **impregnably** (adv.): uneinnehmbar.
   bars (pl.): Gitter.
15 **stunned:** besinnungslos.
16f. **to transcend s.th.:** über etwas hinausgehen.
19 **bunting:** Flaggen.

dress. Whit-Monday had been looked forward to for a
month or more. By the afternoon even those who be-
lieved in the Unseen were beginning to resume their little amusements in a tentative fashion, on the supposition
5 that he had quite gone away, and with the sceptics he was
already a jest. But people, sceptics and believers alike,
were remarkably sociable all that day.

Haysman's meadow was gay with a tent, in which Mrs.
Bunting and other ladies were preparing tea, while,
10 without, the Sunday-school children ran races and
played games under the noisy guidance of the curate and
the Misses Cuss and Sackbut. No doubt there was a
slight uneasiness in the air, but people for the most part
had the sense to conceal whatever imaginative qualms
15 they experienced. On the village green an inclined
string, down which, clinging the while to a pulley-swung
handle, one could be hurled violently against a sack at
the other end, came in for considerable favour among
the adolescent. There were swings and cocoanut shies
20 and promenading, and the steam organ attached to the

---

4   **supposition:** Annahme, Vermutung.
6   **jest:** Scherz.
11 **curate:** Pfarrer.
13 **uneasiness:** (ängstliches) Unbehagen; Unruhe.
14 **qualm:** Skrupel, Bedenken.
15 **village green:** Dorfwiese.
    inclined: schief(gespannt).
16f. **pulley-swung handle:** schwingender, an einem Flaschenzug aufge-
    hängter Griff.
18 **to come in for favour:** Zuspruch finden.
19 **adolescent:** Jugendlicher; hier: Jugend, junge Leute.
20 **steam organ:** Dampforgel (mit einer Dampfmaschine betriebene Or-
    gel auf Jahrmärkten).

swings filled the air with a pungent flavour of oil and with equally pungent music. Members of the Club, who had attended church in the morning, were splendid in badges of pink and green, and some of the gayer-minded
5 had also adorned their bowler hats with brilliant-coloured favours of ribbon. Old Fletcher, whose conceptions of holiday-making were severe, was visible through the jasmine about his window or through the open door (whichever way you chose to look), poised delicately on
0 a plank supported on two chairs, and whitewashing the ceiling of his front room.

About four o'clock a stranger entered the village from the direction of the downs. He was a short, stout person in an extraordinarily shabby top hat, and he appeared to
5 be very much out of breath. His cheeks were alternately limp and tightly puffed. His mottled face was apprehensive, and he moved with a sort of reluctant alacrity. He turned the corner by the church, and directed his way to the Coach and Horses. Among others old Fletcher re-
0 members seeing him, and indeed the old gentleman was

---

1 **flavour:** Geruch.
4 **badge:** Abzeichen.
5 **to adorn:** schmücken, zieren.
6 **favour:** Schleife.
9 (*to be*) **poised:** balancieren.
  delicately (adv.): behutsam, vorsichtig.
10 **to whitewash:** (weiß) tünchen.
14 **top hat:** Zylinder.
15 **alternately** (adv.): abwechselnd.
16 **tightly puffed:** straff aufgeblasen.
   mottled: fleckig.
16f. **apprehensive:** ängstlich.
17 **alacrity:** Eile, Eifer.

so struck by his peculiar agitation that he inadvertently
allowed a quantity of whitewash to run down the brush
into the sleeve of his coat while regarding him.

This stranger, to the perceptions of the proprietor of the
5 cocoanut shy, appeared to be talking to himself, and Mr.
Huxter remarked the same thing. He stopped at the foot
of the Coach and Horses steps, and, according to Mr.
Huxter, appeared to undergo a severe internal struggle
before he could induce himself to enter the house. Fi-
10 nally he marched up the steps, and was seen by Mr. Huxter to turn to the left and open the door of the parlour.
Mr. Huxter heard voices from within the room and from
the bar apprising the man of his error. "That room's private!" said Hall, and the stranger shut the door clumsily
15 and went into the bar.

In the course of a few minutes he reappeared, wiping his
lips with the back of his hand with an air of quiet satisfaction that somehow impressed Mr. Huxter as assumed.
He stood looking about him for some moments, and
20 then Mr. Huxter saw him walk in an oddly furtive manner towards the gates of the yard, upon which the parlour window opened. The stranger, after some hesitation, leant against one of the gate-posts, produced a
short clay pipe, and prepared to fill it. His fingers trem-

---

1 **agitation:** Aufregung.
  inadvertently (adv.): unachtsam.
2 **whitewash:** (weiße) Tünche.
8 **to undergo:** erfahren, erleben, durchmachen.
9 **to induce o.s. to do s.th.:** sich dazu bringen, etwas zu tun.
13 **to apprise s.o.:** jdn. in Kenntnis setzen.
14 **clumsily** (adv.): schwerfällig, unbeholfen.
18 **assumed:** vorgetäuscht, unnatürlich, gespielt.
20 **furtive:** heimlichtuerisch, verstohlen.

bled while doing so. He lit it clumsily, and folding his arms began to smoke in a languid attitude, an attitude which his occasional quick glances up the yard altogether belied.

5 All this Mr. Huxter saw over the canisters of the tobacco window, and the singularity of the man's behaviour prompted him to maintain his observation.

Presently the stranger stood up abruptly and put his pipe in his pocket. Then he vanished into the yard. Forthwith
10 Mr. Huxter, conceiving he was witness of some petty larceny, leapt round his counter and ran out into the road to intercept the thief. As he did so, Mr. Marvel reappeared, his hat askew, a big bundle in a blue table-cloth in one hand, and three books tied together – as it proved
15 afterwards with the Vicar's braces – in the other. Directly he saw Huxter he gave a sort of gasp, and turning sharply to the left, began to run. "Stop thief!" cried Huxter, and set off after him. Mr. Huxter's sensations were vivid but brief. He saw the man just before him and spurting
20 briskly for the church corner and the hill road. He saw the village flags and festivities beyond, and a face or so turned towards him. He bawled, "Stop!" again. He had hardly gone ten strides before his shin was caught in

---

2 **languid:** träge, nachlässig.
4 **to belie:** Lügen strafen.
5 **canister:** Behälter, Büchse.
6 **singularity:** Merkwürdigkeit, Sonderbarkeit.
7 **to promt s.o. to do s.th.:** jdn. veranlassen, etwas zu tun.
10 **to conceive:** sich vorstellen, begreifen.
10 f. **petty larceny:** leichter Diebstahl.
12 **to intercept s.o.:** jdn. abfangen.
13 **askew:** schief, auf der Seite.
15 **braces** (pl.): Hosenträger.
22 **to bawl:** brüllen.

some mysterious fashion, and he was no longer running, but flying with inconceivable rapidity through the air. He saw the ground suddenly close to his face. The world seemed to splash into a million whirling specks of light, and subsequent proceedings interested him no more.

Chapter XI

In the "Coach and Horses"

Now in order clearly to understand what had happened in the inn, it is necessary to go back to the moment when Mr. Marvel first came into view of Mr. Huxter's window. At that precise moment Mr. Cuss and Mr. Bunting were in the parlour. They were seriously investigating the strange occurrences of the morning, and were, with Mr. Hall's permission, making a thorough examination of the Invisible Man's belongings. Jaffers had partially recovered from his fall and had gone home in the charge of his sympathetic friends. The stranger's scattered garments had been removed by Mrs. Hall and the room tidied up. And on the table under the window where the stranger had been wont to work, Cuss had hit almost at once on three big books in manuscript labelled "Diary."

"Diary!" said Cuss, putting the three books on the table.

---

4 **speck:** Fleck.
5 **proceedings:** Ereignisse.
15 **partially** (adv.): teilweise.
16 **in the charge of s.o.:** in der Obhut von jdm.

"Now, at any rate, we shall learn something." The Vicar stood with his hands on the table.

"Diary," repeated Cuss, sitting down, putting two volumes to support the third, and opening it. "H'm – no name on the fly-leaf. Bother! – cypher. And figures."

The Vicar came round to look over his shoulder.

Cuss turned the pages over with a face suddenly disappointed. "I'm – dear me! It's all cypher, Bunting."

"There are no diagrams?" asked Mr. Bunting. "No illustrations throwing light —"

"See for yourself," said Mr. Cuss. "Some of it's mathematical and some of it's Russian or some such language (to judge by the letters), and some of it's Greek. Now the Greek I thought *you* —"

"Of course," said Mr. Bunting, taking out and wiping his spectacles and feeling suddenly very uncomfortable, – for he had no Greek left in his mind worth talking about; "yes – the Greek, of course, may furnish a clue."

"I'll find you a place."

"I'd rather glance through the volumes first," said Mr. Bunting, still wiping. "A general impression first, Cuss, and *then*, you know, we can go looking for clues."

He coughed, put on his glasses, arranged them fastidiously, coughed again, and wished something would happen to avert the seemingly inevitable exposure. Then he

---

4 **volume:** (Buch-)Band.
5 **fly-leaf:** Vorsatzblatt, erstes Blatt eines Buches.
   bother! (infml.): wie ärgerlich!
   cypher: Geheimschrift.
19 **clue:** Anhaltspunkt.
24f. **fastidiously** (adv.): umständlich, wählerisch.
26 **to avert:** (Schaden) abwenden.
   exposure: Bloßstellung, Blamage.

took the volume Cuss handed him in a leisurely manner.
And then something did happen.

The door opened suddenly.

Both gentlemen started violently, looked round, and
were relieved to see a sporadically rosy face beneath
a furry silk hat. "Tap?" asked the face, and stood
staring.

"No," said both gentlemen at once.

"Over the other side, my man," said Mr. Bunting. And
"Please shut that door," said Mr. Cuss, irritably.

"All right," said the intruder, as it seemed, in a low voice
curiously different from the huskiness of its first inquiry.
"Right you are," said the intruder in the former voice.
"Stand clear!" and he vanished and closed the door.

"A sailor, I should judge," said Mr. Bunting. "Amusing
fellows they are. Stand clear! indeed. A nautical term re-
ferring to his getting back out of the room, I suppose."

"I daresay so," said Cuss. "My nerves are all loose to-
day. It quite made me jump – the door opening like
that."

Mr. Bunting smiled as if he had not jumped. "And now,"
he said with a sigh, "these books."

"One minute," said Cuss, and went and locked the door.
"Now I think we are safe from interruption."

Some one sniffed as he did so.

---

5 **sporadically rosy:** rotgefleckt (*sporadically* [adv.]: vereinzelt vorkom-
     mend, hin und wieder).
6 **tap:** *tap-room:* Schankraum.
10 **irritably** (adv.): reizbar.
11 **intruder:** Eindringling.
12 **huskiness:** Heiserkeit.
14 **stand clear!:** aus dem Weg!
16 **nautical term:** seemännischer (Fach-)Ausdruck.

"One thing is indisputable," said Bunting, drawing up a chair next to that of Cuss. "There certainly have been very strange things happen in Iping during the last few days – very strange. I cannot of course believe in this absurd invisibility story —"

"It's incredible," said Cuss, "– incredible. But the fact remains that I saw – I certainly saw right down his sleeve —"

"But did you – are you sure? Suppose a mirror, for instance, – hallucinations are so easily produced. I don't know if you have ever seen a really good conjuror —"

"I won't argue again," said Cuss. "We've thrashed that out, Bunting. And just now there's these books – Ah! here's some of what I take to be Greek! Greek letters certainly."

He pointed to the middle of the page. Mr. Bunting flushed slightly and brought his face nearer, apparently finding some difficulty with his glasses. Suddenly he became aware of a strange feeling at the nape of his neck. He tried to raise his head, and encountered an immovable resistance. The feeling was a curious pressure, the grip of a heavy, firm hand, and it bore his chin irresistibly to the table. "*Don't move, little men,*" whispered a voice, "*or I'll brain you both!*" He looked into the face of Cuss,

---

11 **conjuror:** Zauberkünstler.
12f. **to thrash s.th. out** (fig.): etwas mehr als genug diskutieren, ausdiskutieren (von *to thrash* ›dreschen‹).
17 **to flush:** erröten.
19 **nape of the neck:** Nacken, Genick.
20 **to encounter:** (auf etwas) treffen, stoßen.
22f. **to bear s.o.'s chin to the table:** jds. Kinn auf den Tisch niederdrücken.
24 **to brain s.o.:** jdm. den Schädel einschlagen.

close to his own, and each saw a horrified reflection of
his own sickly astonishment.

"I'm sorry to handle you roughly," said the Voice, "but
it's unavoidable.

Since when did you learn to pry into an investigator's
private memoranda?" said the Voice; and two chins
struck the table simultaneously, and two sets of teeth rat-
tled.

"Since when did you learn to invade the private rooms
of a man in misfortune?" and the concussion was repeated.

"Where have they put my clothes?

Listen," said the Voice. "The windows are fastened and
I've taken the key out of the door. I am a fairly strong
man, and I have the poker handy – besides being invisible. There's not the slightest doubt that I could kill you
both and get away quite easily if I wanted to – do you
understand? Very well. If I let you go will you promise
not to try any nonsense and do what I tell you?"

The Vicar and the Doctor looked at one another, and the
Doctor pulled a face. "Yes," said Mr. Bunting, and the
Doctor repeated it. Then the pressure on the necks relaxed, and the Doctor and the Vicar sat up, both very red
in the face and wriggling their heads.

"Please keep sitting where you are," said the Invisible
Man. "Here's the poker, you see.

When I come into this room," continued the Invisible

---

2 **sickly:** blaß (Gesicht).
5 **to pry into s.th.:** in etwas eindringen, herumstöbern, -spionieren.
6 **memoranda** (Lat.): Aufzeichnungen.
7 **simultaneously** (adv.): gleichzeitig.
15 **to have s.th. handy** etwas griffbereit haben.
24 **to wriggle:** kreisen lassen, hin und her bewegen; hier auch: schütteln.

Man, after presenting the poker to the tip of the nose of each of his visitors, "I did not expect to find it occupied, and I expected to find, in addition to my books of memoranda, an outfit of clothing. Where is it? No, – don't rise. I can see it's gone. Now, just at present, though the days are quite warm enough for an invisible man to run about stark, the evenings are chilly. I want clothing – and other accommodation; and I must also have those three books."

Chapter XII

The Invisible Man Loses his Temper

It is unavoidable that at this point the narrative should break off again, for a certain very painful reason that will presently be apparent. While these things were going on in the parlour, and while Mr. Huxter was watching Mr. Marvel smoking his pipe against the gate, not a dozen yards away were Mr. Hall and Teddy Henfrey discussing in a state of cloudy puzzlement the one Iping topic. Suddenly there came a violent thud against the door of the parlour, a sharp cry, and then – silence.

"*Hul* –lo!" said Teddy Henfrey.

"*Hul – lo!*" from the Tap.

---

7 **stark** (auch: *stark naked*): splitternackt.
8 **accomodation:** hier: Versorgung, notwendige Dinge.
12 **narrative:** Erzählung.
18 **cloudy:** verworren.
19 **thud:** dumpfer Schlag.

Mr. Hall took things in slowly but surely. "That ain't right," he said, and came round from behind the bar towards the parlour door.

He and Teddy approached the door together, with intent
5 faces. Their eyes considered. "Summat wrong," said Hall, and Henfrey nodded agreement. Whiffs of an unpleasant chemical odour met them, and there was a muffled sound of conversation, very rapid and subdued.

"You all raight thur?" asked Hall, rapping.

10 The muttered conversation ceased abruptly, for a moment silence, then the conversation was resumed in hissing whispers, then a sharp cry of "No! no, you don't!" There came a sudden motion and the oversetting of a chair, a brief struggle. Silence again.

15 "What the dooce?" exclaimed Henfrey, *sotto voce*.

"You – all – raight – thur?" asked Mr. Hall sharply, again.

The Vicar's voice answered with a curious jerking intonation: "Quite ri – ight. Please don't – interrupt."

20 "Odd!" said Mr. Henfrey.

"Odd!" said Mr. Hall.

"Says, 'Don't interrupt,'" said Henfrey.

"I heerd 'n," said Hall.

"And a sniff," said Henfrey.

25 They remained listening. The conversation was rapid

---

1 **to take s.th. in:** etwas begreifen.
5 **summat** (dial.): *somewhat: something.*
6 **whiff:** Hauch, Wolke, Schwade.
8 **subdued:** mit unterdrückter Stimme geführt.
9 **You all raight thur?** (dial.): *Are you all right there?*
15 **sotto voce** (Ital., adv.): leise, halblaut.
18 **jerking:** ruckartig.
23 **I heerd 'n** (dial.): *I heard him.*

and subdued. "I *can't*," said Mr. Bunting, his voice rising; "I tell you, sir, I *will* not."

"What was that?" asked Henfrey.

"Says he wi' nart," said Hall. "Warn't speakin' to us, wuz he?"

"Disgraceful!" said Mr. Bunting, within.

"'Disgraceful,'" said Mr. Henfrey. "I heard it – *distinct*."

"Who's that speaking now?" asked Henfrey.

"Mr. Cuss, I s'pose," said Hall. "Can you hear – anything?"

Silence. The sounds within indistinct and perplexing.

"Sounds like throwing the table-cloth about," said Hall.

Mrs. Hall appeared behind the bar. Hall made gestures of silence and invitation. This roused Mrs. Hall's wifely opposition. "What yer listenin' there for, Hall?" she asked. "Ain't you nothin' better to do – busy day like this?"

Hall tried to convey everything by grimaces and dumb show, but Mrs. Hall was obdurate. She raised her voice. So Hall and Henfrey, rather crestfallen, tiptoed back to the bar, gesticulating to explain to her.

At first she refused to see anything in what they had heard at all. Then she insisted on Hall keeping silence, while Henfrey told her his story. She was inclined to

---

4 **wi' nart** (dial.): *will not*.
   warn't (dial.): *was not*.
12 **perplexing:** verwirrend, verworren.
20 f. **dumb show:** Pantomime.
21 **obdurate:** unnachgiebig, unerbittlich.
22 **crestfallen:** geknickt, kleinlaut.
   to tiptoe: auf Zehenspitzen gehen.

think the whole business nonsense – perhaps they were
just moving the furniture about. "I heerd 'n say 'disgraceful'; *that* I did," said Hall.

"*I* heerd that, Mis' Hall," said Henfrey.

5 "Like as not –" began Mrs. Hall.

"Hsh!" said Mr. Teddy Henfrey. "Didn't I hear the window?"

"What window?" asked Mrs. Hall.

"Parlour window," said Henfrey.

10 Everyone stood listening intently. Mrs. Hall's eyes, directed straight before her, saw without seeing the brilliant oblong of the inn door, the road white and vivid,
and Huxter's shop-front blistering in the June sun.
Abruptly Huxter's door opened and Huxter appeared,

15 eyes staring with excitement, arms gesticulating. "*Yap!*"
cried Huxter. "Stop thief!" and he ran obliquely across
the oblong towards the yard gates, and vanished.
Simultaneously came a tumult from the parlour, and a
sound of windows being closed.

20 Hall, Henfrey, and the human contents of the Tap
rushed out at once pell-mell into the street. They saw
some one whisk round the corner towards the down
road, and Mr. Huxter executing a complicated leap in
the air that ended on his face and shoulder. Down the

25 street people were standing astonished or running towards them.

Mr. Huxter was stunned. Henfrey stopped to discover

5 **like as not:** was ist Besonderes dabei?
12 **oblong:** Rechteck.
13 **to blister:** gleißen.
15 **yap:** 1. Ausruf; etwa: he! halt!; 2. (dial.) Tölpel.
16 **obliquely** (adv.): quer, schräg.
21 **pell-mell** (adv.): durcheinander.

this, but Hall and the two labourers from the Tap rushed at once to the corner, shouting incoherent things, and saw Mr. Marvel vanishing by the corner of the church wall. They appear to have jumped to the impossible conclusion that this was the Invisible Man suddenly become visible, and set off at once along the lane in pursuit. But Hall had hardly run a dozen yards before he gave a loud shout of astonishment and went flying headlong sideways, clutching one of the labourers and bringing him to the ground. He had been charged just as one charges a man at football. The second labourer came round in a circle, stared, and conceiving that Hall had tumbled over of his own accord, turned to resume the pursuit, only to be tripped by the ankle just as Huxter had been. Then, as the first labourer struggled to his feet, he was kicked sideways by a blow that might have felled an ox.

As he went down, the rush from the direction of the village green came round the corner. The first to appear was the proprietor of the cocoanut shy, a burly man in a blue jersey. He was astonished to see the lane empty save for three men sprawling absurdly on the ground. And then something happened to his rear-most foot, and he went headlong and rolled sideways just in time to graze the feet of his brother and partner, following headlong. The two were then kicked, knelt on, fallen over, and cursed by quite a number of over-hasty people.

4 f. **to jump to a conclusion:** zu einer Schlußfolgerung gelangen.
14 **ankle:** Fußknöchel.
16 **to fell:** niederstrecken.
19 **burly:** kräftig.
21 **to sprawl:** ausgestreckt daliegen.
22 **rear-most:** hinterste(r, -s).
24 **to graze:** streifen.

Now when Hall and Henfrey and the labourers ran
out of the house, Mrs. Hall, who had been disciplined
by years of experience, remained in the bar next the
till. And suddenly the parlour door was opened, and
5 Mr. Cuss appeared, and without glancing at her rushed
at once down the steps towards the corner. "Hold him!"
he cried. "Don't let him drop that parcel! You can
see him so long as he holds the parcel." He knew
nothing of the existence of Marvel. For the Invisible
10 Man had handed over the books and bundle in the yard.
The face of Mr. Cuss was angry and resolute, but his costume was defective, a sort of limp white kilt that could
only have passed muster in Greece. "Hold him!" he
bawled. "He's got my trousers! And every stitch of the
15 Vicar's clothes!
'Tend to him in a minute!" he cried to Henfrey as he
passed the prostrate Huxter, and coming round the corner to join the tumult, was promptly knocked off his feet
into an indecorous sprawl. Somebody in full flight trod
20 heavily on his finger. He yelled, struggled to regain his
feet, was knocked against and thrown on all fours again,
and became aware that he was involved not in a capture,
but a rout. Everyone was running back to the village. He
rose again and was hit severely behind the ear. He stag-
25 gered and set off back to the Coach and Horses forth-

---

4 **till:** Geldschublade.
12 **defective:** fehler-, mangelhaft.
   kilt: eigtl.: Schottenrock; hier: Kittel.
13 **to pass muster:** durchgehen, den Anforderungen genügen.
14 **stitch** (infml.): Faden.
19 **indecorous:** unschicklich, unästhetisch.
   sprawl: ausgestreckte Bodenlage.
22 **capture:** Gefangennahme.

with, leaping over the deserted Huxter, who was now sitting up, on his way.

Behind him as he was halfway up the inn steps he heard a sudden yell of rage, rising sharply out of the confusion of cries, and a sounding smack in someone's face. He recognised the voice as that of the Invisible Man, and the note was that of a man suddenly infuriated by a painful blow.

In another moment Mr. Cuss was back in the parlour. "He's coming back, Bunting!" he said, rushing in. "Save yourself! He's gone mad!"

Mr. Bunting was standing in the window engaged in an attempt to clothe himself in the hearth-rug and a West Surrey Gazette. "Who's coming?" he said, so startled that his costume narrowly escaped disintegration.

"Invisible Man," said Cuss, and rushed to the window. "We'd better clear out from here! He's fighting mad! Mad!"

In another moment he was out in the yard.

"Good heavens!" said Mr. Bunting, hesitating between two horrible alternatives. He heard a frightful struggle in the passage of the inn, and his decision was made. He clambered out of the window, adjusted his costume hastily, and fled up the village as fast as his fat little legs would carry him.

---

 1 **deserted:** allein gelassen.
 5 **smack:** Schlag.
 7 **to infuriate:** wütend machen, erzürnen.
13 **hearth-rug:** Kaminvorleger.
13f. **West Surrey Gazette:** Name einer Zeitung.
15 **disintegration: A**uflösung; hier auch: Herunterfallen.
17 **to clear out** (infml.): verschwinden, sich davonmachen.
23 **to clamber:** klettern.
   to adjust: in Ordnung bringen, zurechtrücken.

From the moment when the Invisible Man screamed
with rage and Mr. Bunting made his memorable flight up
the village, it became impossible to give a consecutive
account of affairs in Iping. Possibly the Invisible Man's
5 original intention was simply to cover Marvel's retreat
with the clothes and books. But his temper, at no time
very good, seems to have gone completely at some
chance blow, and forthwith he set to smiting and over-
throwing, for the mere satisfaction of hurting.

10 You must figure the street full of running figures, of
doors slamming and fights for hiding-places. You must
figure the tumult suddenly striking on the unstable equilibrium of old Fletcher's planks and two chairs, – with
cataclysmal results. You must figure an appalled couple
15 caught dismally in a swing. And then the whole tumultuous rush has passed and the Iping street with its gauds
and flags is deserted save for the still raging Unseen, and
littered with cocoanuts, overthrown canvas screens, and
the scattered stock in trade of a sweetstuff stall. Every-
20 where there is a sound of closing shutters and shoving

---

3 **consecutive:** zusammenhängend, folgerichtig.
5 **to cover:** decken, verbergen.
8 **chance:** zufällig.
12f. **unstable equilibrium:** unstabiles Gleichgewicht, wackelige Lage.
14 **cataclysmal:** katastrophal.
   appalled: entsetzt.
15 **dismally** (adv.): kläglich.
15f. **tumultuous:** heftig, stürmisch.
16 **gaud:** Schmuck.
18 **littered:** übersät.
   canvas screen: Zeltbahn.
19 **stock in trade:** Waren.
   stall: (Verkaufs-)Stand.
20 **to shove:** zu-, vorschieben.

bolts, and the only visible humanity is an occasional flitting eye under a raised eyebrow in the corner of a window pane.

The Invisible Man amused himself for a little while by breaking all the windows in the Coach and Horses, and then he thrust a street lamp through the parlour window of Mrs. Gribble. He it must have been who cut the telegraph wire to Adderdean just beyond Higgins' cottage on the Adderdean road. And after that, as his peculiar qualities allowed, he passed out of human perceptions altogether, and he was neither heard, seen, nor felt in Iping any more. He vanished absolutely.

But it was the best part of two hours before any human being ventured out again into the desolation of Iping street.

Chapter XIII

Mr. Marvel Discusses his Resignation

When the dusk was gathering and Iping was just beginning to peep timorously forth again upon the shattered wreckage of its Bank Holiday, a short, thickset man in a shabby silk hat was marching painfully through the twi-

---

1 f. **to flit:** zucken, flattern.
19 **to shatter:** zerschlagen, zertrümmern.
20 **wreckage:** (fig.) Wrack, (zertrümmerter) Überrest.
    Bank Holiday: offizieller, nicht auf einen Samstag oder Sonntag fallender Feiertag (in der Regel Montag), an dem Banken und Postämter sowie die meisten Geschäfte geschlossen sind.
    thickset: gedrungen.

light behind the beechwoods on the road to Bramblehurst. He carried three books bound together by some
sort of ornamental elastic ligature, and a bundle
wrapped in a blue table-cloth. His rubicund face ex-
5 pressed consternation and fatigue; he appeared to be in
a spasmodic sort of hurry. He was accompanied by a
Voice other than his own, and ever and again he winced
under the touch of unseen hands.

"If you give me the slip again," said the Voice; "if you at-
10 tempt to give me the slip again —"

"Lord!" said Mr. Marvel. "That shoulder's a mass of
bruises as it is."

"– on my honour," said the Voice, "I will kill you."

"I didn't try to give you the slip," said Marvel, in a voice
15 that was not far remote from tears. "I swear I didn't. I
didn't know the blessed turning, that was all! How the
devil was I to know the blessed turning? As it is, I've
been knocked about —"

"You'll get knocked about a great deal more if you don't
20 mind," said the Voice, and Mr. Marvel abruptly became
silent. He blew out his cheeks, and his eyes were eloquent of despair.

"It's bad enough to let these floundering yokels explode

---

1 **beechwoods:** Buchenwälder.
3 **ligature:** Band.
4 **rubicund:** rot.
5 **consternation:** Bestürzung.
7 **to wince:** zusammenzucken.
9 **to give s.o. the slip** (infml.): jdm. entwischen.
12 **bruise:** blauer Fleck, Bluterguß.
23 **floundering:** (fig.) ungeschickt, einfältig.
 yokel (pej.): Bauerntölpel.
23 f. **to explode a secret** (fig.): ein Geheimnis entlarven, hinter ein Geheimnis kommen.

my little secret, without *your* cutting off with my books.
It's lucky for some of them they cut and ran when they
did! Here am I – No one knew I was invisible! And now
what am I to do?"

"What am *I* to do?" asked Marvel, *sotto voce*.

"It's all about. It will be in the papers! Everybody will be
looking for me; everyone on their guard –" The Voice
broke off into vivid curses and ceased.

The despair of Mr. Marvel's face deepened, and his pace
slacked.

"Go on!" said the Voice.

Mr. Marvel's face assumed a greyish tint between the
ruddier patches.

"Don't drop those books, stupid," said the Voice,
sharply – overtaking him.

"The fact is," said the Voice, "I shall have to make use of
you. You're a poor tool, but I must."

"I'm a *miserable* tool," said Marvel.

"You are," said the Voice.

"I'm the worst possible tool you could have," said Marvel.

"I'm not strong," he said after a discouraging silence.

"I'm not over-strong," he repeated.

"No?"

"And my heart's weak. That little business – I pulled
it through, of course – but bless you! I could have
dropped."

"Well?"

---

1 **to cut off:** sich davonmachen.

7 (*to be*) **on one's guard:** auf der Hut sein.

10 **to slack:** sich verlangsamen.

12 **tint:** leichte Färbung.

"I haven't the nerve and strength for the sort of thing you want."

"*I'll* stimulate you."

"I wish you wouldn't. I wouldn't like to mess up your
5 plans, you know. But I might, – out of sheer funk and misery."

"You'd better not," said the Voice, with quiet emphasis.

"I wish I was dead," said Marvel.

"It ain't justice," he said; "you must admit – It seems to
10 me I've a perfect right —"

"*Get* on!" said the Voice.

Mr. Marvel mended his pace, and for a time they went in silence again.

"It's devilish hard," said Mr. Marvel.

15 This was quite ineffectual. He tried another tack.

"What do I make by it?" he began again in a tone of un-endurable wrong.

"Oh! *shut up!*" said he Voice, with sudden amazing vigour. "I'll see to you all right. You do what you're
20 told. You'll do it all right. You're a fool and all that, but you'll do —"

"I tell you, sir, I'm not the man for it. Respectfully – but it is so —"

"If you don't shut up I shall twist your wrist again," said
25 the Invisible Man. "I want to think."

Presently two oblongs of yellow light appeared through

---

1 **nerve:** Nerven, Mut.
4 **to mess up:** (Plan) durcheinanderbringen.
5 **funk** (infml.): Bammel, Schiß.
12 **to mend one's pace:** den Schritt beschleunigen.
15 **ineffectual:** wirkungslos.
   to try another tack: (fig.) einen anderen Weg versuchen.
16 **What do I make by it?:** Was habe ich davon?

the trees, and the square tower of a church loomed through the gloaming. "I shall keep my hand on your shoulder," said the Voice, "all through the village. Go straight through and try no foolery. It will be the worse for you if you do."

"I know that," sighed Mr. Marvel, "I know all that."

The unhappy-looking figure in the obsolete silk hat passed up the street of the little village with his burdens, and vanished into the gathering darkness beyond the lights of the windows.

Chapter XIV

At Port Stowe

Ten o'clock the next morning found Mr. Marvel, unshaven, dirty, and travel-stained, sitting with the books beside him and his hands deep in his pockets, looking very weary, nervous, and uncomfortable, and inflating his cheeks at frequent intervals, on the bench outside a little inn on the outskirts of Port Stowe. Beside him were the books, but now they were tied with string. The bundle had been abandoned in the pinewoods beyond Bramblehurst, in accordance with a change in the plans

---

1 **to loom:** sichtbar werden, sich abzeichnen.
2 **gloaming:** (Abend-)Dämmerung.
7 **obsolete:** veraltet, altmodisch.
16 **to inflate:** aufblasen.
18 **outskirts:** Außenbezirk(e).
20 **pinewoods:** Kiefernwälder.

of the Invisible Man. Mr. Marvel sat on the bench, and
although no one took the slightest notice of him, his
agitation remained at fever heat. His hands would go
ever and again to his various pockets with a curious
5 nervous fumbling.
When he had been sitting for the best part of an hour
however, an elderly mariner, carrying a newspaper, came
out of the inn and sat down beside him. "Pleasant day,"
said the mariner.
10 Mr. Marvel glanced about him with something very like
terror. "Very," he said.
"Just seasonable weather for the time of year," said the
mariner, taking no denial.
"Quite," said Mr. Marvel.
15 The mariner produced a toothpick, and (saving his regard) was engrossed thereby for some minutes. His eyes
meanwhile were at liberty to examine Mr. Marvel's dusty
figure and the books beside him. As he had approached
Mr. Marvel he had heard a sound like the dropping
20 of coins into a pocket. He was struck by the contrast
of Mr. Marvel's appearance with this suggestion of
opulence. Thence his mind wandered back again to a
topic that had taken a curiously firm hold of his imagination.
25 "Books?" he said suddenly, noisily finishing with the
toothpick.

---

7 **mariner:** Seemann.
12 **seasonable:** der Jahreszeit entsprechend.
15 **toothpick:** Zahnstocher.
15f. **to save one's regard:** den Blick nicht abwenden.
16 **to be engrossed:** (fig.) vertieft sein.
22 **opulence:** Wohlhabenheit, Wohlstand.
     thence (arch.): von da.

Mr. Marvel started and looked at them. "Oh, yes," he said. "Yes, they're books."

"There's some extra-ordinary things in books," said the mariner.

"I believe you," said Mr. Marvel.

"And some extra-ordinary things out of 'em," said the mariner.

"True likewise," said Mr. Marvel. He eyed his interlocutor, and then glanced about him.

"There's some extra-ordinary things in newspapers, for example," sait the mariner.

"There are."

"In *this* newspaper," said the mariner.

"Ah!" said Mr. Marvel.

"There's a story," said the mariner, fixing Mr. Marvel with an eye that was firm and deliberate; "there's a story about an Invisible Man, for instance."

Mr. Marvel pulled his mouth askew and scratched his cheek and felt his ears glowing. "What will they be writing next?" he asked faintly. "Ostria, or America?"

"Neither," said the mariner. "*Here!*"

"Lord!" said Mr. Marvel, starting.

"When I say *here*," said the mariner, to Mr. Marvel's intense relief, "I don't of course mean here in this place, I mean hereabouts."

"An Invisible Man!" said Mr. Marvel. "And what's *he* been up to?"

"Everything," said the mariner, controlling Marvel with his eye, and then amplifying: "Every Blessed Thing."

---

8 **likewise** (adv.): ebenfalls.
20 **Ostria** (dial.): *Austria; Australia.*
27 **to be up to s.th.:** etwas vorhaben, im Schilde führen.
29 **to amplify:** ausführen, näher erläutern.

"I ain't seen a paper these four days," said Marvel.

"Iping's the place he started at," said the mariner.

"In-*deed!*" said Mr. Marvel.

"He started there. And where he came from, nobody
5 don't seem to know. Here it is: Pe Culiar Story from Iping. And it says in this paper that the evidence is extra-
ordinary strong – extra-ordinary."

"Lord!" said Mr. Marvel.

"But then, it's a extra-ordinary story. There is a clergy-
10 man and a medical gent witnesses, – saw 'im all right and
proper – or leastways, didn't see 'im. He was staying, it
says, at the Coach an' Horses, and no one don't seem to
have been aware of his misfortune, it says, aware of his
misfortune, until in an Alteration in the inn, it says, his
15 bandages on his head was torn off. It was then ob-served
that his head was invisible. Attempts were At Once
made to secure him, but casting off his garments it says,
he succeeded in escaping, but not until after a desperate
struggle, In Which he had inflicted serious injuries, it
20 says, on our worthy and able constable, Mr. J. A. Jaffers.
Pretty straight story, eigh? Names and everything."

"Lord!" said Mr. Marvel, looking nervously about him,
trying to count the money in his pockets by his unaided
sense of touch, and full of a strange and novel idea. "It
25 sounds most astonishing."

---

6 **evidence:** Aussagen, Belege.
9f. **clergyman:** Pfarrer, Geistlicher.
10 **gent:** Kurzform von *gentleman.*
11 **leastways** (adv., infml.): vielmehr.
14 **alteration** (dial.): gemeint ist *altercation:* Streit.
17 **to secure:** (Gefangenen) fesseln.
19 **to inflict s.th. on s.o.:** jdm. etwas zufügen.
21 **straight:** unmißverständlich, klar.
24 **novel:** neu.

"Don't it? Extra-ordinary, *I* call it. Never heard tell of Invisible Men before, I haven't, but nowadays one hears such a lot of extra-ordinary things – that —"

"That all he did?" asked Marvel, trying to seem at his ease.

"It's enough, ain't it?" said the mariner.

"Didn't go Back by any chance?" asked Marvel. "Just escaped and that's all, eh?"

"All!" said the mariner. "Why! – ain't it enough?"

"Quite enough," said Marvel.

"I should think it was enough," said the mariner. "I should think it was enough."

"He didn't have any pals – it don't say he had any pals, does it?" asked Mr. Marvel, anxious.

"Ain't one of a sort enough for you?" asked the mariner. "No, thank Heaven, as one might say, he didn't."

He nodded his head slowly. "It makes me regular uncomfortable, the bare thought of that chap running about the country! He is at present At Large, and from certain evidence it is supposed that he has – taken – *took*, I suppose they mean – the road to Port Stowe. You see we're right *in* it! None of your American wonders, this time. And just think of the things he might do! Where'd you be, if he took a drop over and above, and had a fancy to go for you? Suppose he wants to rob – who can prevent him? He can trespass, he can burgle, he could walk

---

4f. **at one's ease:** unbefangen.
13 **pal** (infml.): Kumpel, Genosse.
19 **to be at large:** frei umherlaufen.
24 **to take a drop over and above:** einen über den Durst trinken.
24f. **to have a fancy to do s.th.:** auf die Idee kommen, etwas zu tun.
26 **to trespass:** sich unbefugt Eintritt verschaffen.
   to burgle: einbrechen, einen Einbruch begehen.

through a cordon of policemen as easy as me or you
could give the slip to a blind man! Easier! For these here
blind chaps hear uncommon sharp, I'm told. And
wherever there was liquor he fancied —"

5 "He's got a tremenjous advantage, certainly," said Mr.
Marvel. "And – well."

"You're right," said the mariner. "He *has*."

All this time Mr. Marvel had been glancing about him intently, listening for faint footfalls, trying to detect imper-
10 ceptible movements. He seemed on the point of some
great resolution. He coughed behind his hand.

He looked about him again, listened, bent towards the
mariner, and lowered his voice: "The fact of it is – I happen – to know just a thing or two about this Invisible
15 Man. From private sources."

"Oh!" said the mariner, interested. "*You?*"

"Yes," said Mr. Marvel. "Me."

"Indeed!" said the mariner. "And may I ask —"

"You'll be astonished," said Mr. Marvel behind his hand.
20 "It's tremenjous."

"Indeed!" said the mariner.

"The fact is," began Mr. Marvel eagerly in a confidential
undertone. Suddenly his expression changed marvel-
lously. "Ow!" he said. He rose stiffly in his seat. His face
25 was eloquent of physical suffering. "Wow!" he said.

"What's up?" said the mariner, concerned.

"Toothache," said Mr. Marvel, and put his hand to his
ear. He caught hold of his books. "I must be getting on,

---

1 **cordon:** (fig.) Kette.
4 **to fancy s.th.:** Lust auf etwas haben, etwas gern mögen.
5 **tremenjous** (dial.): *tremendous.*
9 **footfall:** Geräusch eines Schritts.
9f. **imperceptible:** unmerklich, kaum wahrnehmbar.

I think," he said. He edged in a curious way along the seat away from his interlocutor. "But you was just a-going to tell me about this here Invisible Man!" protested the mariner. Mr. Marvel seemed to consult with himself. "Hoax," said a voice. "It's a hoax," said Mr. Marvel.

"But it's in the paper," said the mariner.

"Hoax all the same," said Marvel. "I know the chap that started the lie. There ain't no Invisible Man whatsoever – Blimey."

"But how 'bout this paper? D'you mean to say —?"

"Not a word of it," said Marvel, stoutly.

The mariner stared, paper in hand. Mr. Marvel jerkily faced about. "Wait a bit," said the mariner, rising and speaking slowly. "D'you mean to say —?"

"I do," said Mr. Marvel.

"Then why did you let me go on and tell you all this blarsted stuff, then? What d'yer mean by letting a man make a fool of himself like that for? Eigh?"

Mr. Marvel blew out his cheeks. The mariner was suddenly very red indeed; he clenched his hands. "I been talking here this ten minutes," he said; "and you, you little pot-bellied, leathery-faced son of an old boot, couldn't have the elementary manners —"

"Don't you come bandying words with *me*," said Mr. Marvel.

---

5 **hoax:** Scherz, Jux, Ulk.
10 **blimey** (BE, slang): verflucht!, Mensch!
12 **stoutly** (adv.): beharrlich.
13 f. **to face jerkily about:** sich ruckartig umdrehen.
23 **pot-bellied:** dickbäuchig.
    boot: gemeint ist vermutl. *boots:* Stiefelknecht.
25 **to bandy words with s.o.:** mit jdm. böse Worte wechseln.

"Bandying words! I'm a jolly good mind —"

"Come up," said a voice, and Mr. Marvel was suddenly whirled about and started marching off in a curious spasmodic manner. "You'd better move on," said the mariner. "*Who's* moving on?" said Mr. Marvel. He was receding obliquely with a curious hurrying gait, with occasional violent jerks forward. Some way along the road he began a muttered monologue, protests and recriminations.

"Silly devil!" said the mariner, legs wide apart, elbows akimbo, watching the receding figure. "I'll show you, you silly ass, – hoaxing *me!* It's here – on the paper!"

Mr. Marvel retorted incoherently and, receding, was hidden by a bend in the road, but the mariner still stood magnificent in the midst of the way, until the approach of a butcher's cart dislodged him. Then he turned himself towards Port Stowe. "Full of extra-ordinary asses," he said softly to himself. "Just to take me down a bit – that was his silly game – It's on the paper!"

And there was another extraordinary thing he was presently to hear, that had happened quite close to him. And that was a vision of a "fist full of money" (no less) travelling without visible agency, along by the wall at the corner of St. Michael's Lane. A brother mariner had seen

---

1 **I'm a jolly good mind:** ich hätte gute Lust.
5f. **to recede:** sich entfernen.
6 **gait:** Gangart.
8f. **recrimination:** Beschuldigung.
12 **to hoax s.o.:** jdn. zum besten halten, foppen.
13 **to retort:** scharf erwidern.
15 **magnificent:** etwa: (fig.) breitspurig.
16 **to dislodge:** vertreiben.
18 **to take s.o. down:** jdn. ärgern, jdm. eins auswischen.
23 **agency:** Tätigkeit, Wirkung.

this wonderful sight that very morning. He had snatched at the money forthwith and had been knocked headlong, and when he had got to his feet the butterfly money had vanished. Our mariner was in the mood to believe anything, he declared, but that was a bit *too* stiff. Afterwards, however, he began to think things over.

The story of the flying money was true. And all about that neighbourhood, even from the august London and Country Banking Company, from the tills of shops and inns – doors standing that sunny weather entirely open – money had been quietly and dexterously making off that day in handfuls and rouleaux, floating quietly along by walls and shady places, dodging quickly from the approaching eyes of men. And it had, though no man had traced it, invariably ended its mysterious flight in the pocket of that agitated gentleman in the obsolete silk hat, sitting outside the little inn on the outskirts of Port Stowe.

5 **stiff:** ‚stark‘.
8 **august:** illuster, berühmt.
11 **dexterously** (adv.): geschickt.
12 **rouleau** (Fr., pl. *rouleaux*): Geldrolle.
13 **to dodge:** sich entziehen, entkommen.
15 **invariably** (adv.): unweigerlich, ausnahmslos.

Chapter XV

The Man who was Running

In the early evening time Doctor Kemp was sitting in his
study in the belvedere on the hill overlooking Burdock.
5 It was a pleasant little room, with three windows, north,
west, and south, and bookshelves crowded with books
and scientific publications, and a broad writing-table,
and, under the north window, a microscope, glass slips,
minute instruments, some cultures, and scattered bottles
10 of reagents. Doctor Kemp's solar lamp was lit, albeit the
sky was still bright with the sunset light, and his blinds
were up because there was no offence of peering out-
siders to require them pulled down. Doctor Kemp was a
tall and slender young man, with flaxen hair and a mous-
15 tache almost white, and the work he was upon would
earn him, he hoped, the fellowship of the Royal Society,
so highly did he think of it.
And his eye presently wandering from his work caught

---

4 **belvedere:** Gebäudeturm (mit Ausblick auf die Landschaft).
8 **glass slips** (pl.): Glasplättchen.
9 **minute instrument:** Präzisionsinstrument.
10 **reagent:** Reagens (Stoff, der eine bestimmte chemische Reaktion
herbeiführt).
solar lamp: Argand-, Runddochtlampe (1783 von dem schweizeri-
schen Erfinder Aimé Argand [1755–1803] konstruiert).
albeit (poet.): wenn auch, obgleich.
12 **offence:** hier: Gefahr.
14 **flaxen:** flachsblond.
14 f. **moustache:** Oberlippenbart.
16 **fellowship:** Mitgliedschaft.
Royal Society: älteste und bedeutendste wissenschaftliche Gesellschaft in Großbritannien, gegründet 1645.

the sunset blazing at the back of the hill that is over against his own. For a minute perhaps he sat, pen in mouth, admiring the rich golden colour above the crest, and then his attention was attracted by the little figure of
5 a man, inky black, running over the hill-brow towards him. He was a shortish little man, and he wore a high hat, and he was running so fast that his legs verily twinkled.

"Another of those fools," said Doctor Kemp. "Like that ass who ran into me this morning round a corner, with
10 his ''Visible Man a-coming, sir!' I can't imagine what possesses people. One might think we were in the thirteenth century."

He got up, went to the window, and stared at the dusky hillside and the dark little figure tearing down it. "He
15 seems in a confounded hurry," said Doctor Kemp, "but he doesn't seem to be getting on. If his pockets were full of lead, he couldn't run heavier.

"Spurted, sir," said Doctor Kemp.

In another moment the higher of the villas that had
20 clambered up the hill from Burdock had occulted the running figure. He was visible again for a moment, and again, and then again, three times between the three detached houses that came next, and then the terrace hid him.

---

3 **crest:** Kamm, höchster Punkt eines Hügels oder Berges.
5 **hill-brow:** Hügel-, Bergkuppe.
7 **verily** (arch.): wahrlich, fürwahr.
  to twinkle: sich rasch bewegen, flink trippeln.
10f. **what possesses people:** was in die Leute gefahren ist.
14 **hillside:** Abhang.
  to tear: rasen, sausen.
20 **to occult:** verdecken, verbergen.
22f. **detached house:** Einzelhaus.

"Asses!" said Doctor Kemp, swinging round on his heel and walking back to his writing-table.

But those who saw the fugitive nearer, and perceived the abject terror on his perspiring face, being themselves in
5 the open roadway, did not share in the doctor's contempt. By the man pounded, and as he ran he chinked like a well-filled purse that is tossed to and fro. He looked neither to the right nor the left, but his dilated eyes stared straight downhill to where the lamps were
10 being lit, and the people were crowded in the street. And his ill-shaped mouth fell apart, and a glairy foam lay on his lips, and his breath came hoarse and noisy. All he passed stopped and began staring up the road and down, and interrogating one another with an inkling of discom-
15 fort for the reason of his haste.

And then presently, far up the hill, a dog playing in the road yelped and ran under a gate, and as they still wondered something, – a wind – a pad, pad, pad, – a sound like a panting breathing, – rushed by.
20 People screamed. People sprang off the pavement. It passed in shouts, it passed by instinct down the hill. They were shouting in the street before Marvel was halfway there. They were bolting into houses and slamming the

---

3 **fugitive:** Flüchtender, Flüchtling.
4 **abject:** elend, erbärmlich.
  perspiring: schwitzend, in Schweiß gebadet.
6 **to pound by:** vorüberstapfen.
  to chink: klimpern.
7 **to and fro:** hin und her.
8f. **dilated eyes:** weit aufgerissene Augen.
11 **glairy:** klebrig, schleimig.
12 **hoarse:** heiser.
14 **inkling:** (fig.) Anflug, Ahnung.
23 **to bolt:** stürzen, rennen, flüchten.

doors behind them, with the news. He heard it and made
one last desperate spurt. Fear came striding by, rushed
ahead of him, and in a moment had seized the town.
4 "The Invisible Man is coming! *The Invisible Man!*"

Chapter XVI

In the Jolly Cricketers

The Jolly Cricketers is just at the bottom of the hill,
where the tram-lines begin. The barman leant his fat red
arms on the counter and talked of horses with an
10 anaemic cabman, while a black-bearded man in grey
snapped up biscuit and cheese, drank Burton, and con-
versed in American with a policeman off duty.
"What's the shouting about?" said the anaemic cabman
going off at a tangent, trying to see up the hill over the
15 dirty yellow blind in the low window of the inn. Somebody ran by outside. "Fire, perhaps," said the barman.
Footsteps approached, running heavily, the door was
pushed open violently, and Marvel, weeping and dishev-

---

6 **the Jolly Cricketers:** Name eines Gasthauses (wörtl.: die lustigen
  Cricketspieler).
8 **tram-lines:** Straßenbahnschienen (*tram:* von Pferden gezogener
  Straßenbahnwagen).
10 **anaemic:** blutarm, bleichsüchtig.
  cabman: Kutscher.
11 **to snap up:** essen.
  Burton: in Burton-on-Trent hergestelltes Bier.
18f. **dishevelled:** zersaust.

elled, his hat gone, the neck of his coat torn open, rushed
in, made a convulsive turn, and attempted to shut the
door. It was held half open by a strap.

"Coming!" he bawled, his voice shrieking with terror.
5 "He's coming. The 'Visible Man! After me! For Gawd's
sake! Elp! Elp! Elp!"

"Shut the doors," said the policeman. "Who's coming?
What's the row?" He went to the door, released the
strap, and it slammed. The American closed the other
10 door.

"Lemme go inside," said Marvel, staggering and weeping, but still clutching the books. "Lemme go inside.
Lock me in – somewhere. I tell you he's after me. I give
him the slip. He said he'd kill me and he will."

15 "*You're* safe," said the man with the black beard. "The
door's shut. What's it all about?"

"Lemme go inside," said Marvel, and shrieked aloud as
a blow suddenly made the fastened door shiver and was
followed by a hurried rapping and a shouting outside.

20 "Hullo," cried the policeman, "who's there?" Mr. Marvel began to make frantic dives at panels that looked like
doors. "He'll kill me – he's got a knife or something. For
Gawd's sake!"

"Here you are," said the barman. "Come in here." And
25 he held up the flap of the bar.

Mr. Marvel rushed behind the bar as the summons out-

---

2 **convulsive:** krampfartig.
5f. **for Gawd's sake! Elp!** (dial.): *for God's sake! Help!*
8 **row:** Lärm, Krach.
18 **to shiver:** erzittern, erdröhnen.
21 **to make frantic dives at panels:** verzweifelt versuchen, durch die
    Wandverkleidung zu entkommen (*panels:* Paneele, Täfelung).
25 **flap:** Klappe.
26 **summons:** Aufforderung.

side was repeated. "Don't open the door," he screamed.
"*Please* don't open the door. *Where* shall I hide?"

"This, this Invisible Man, then?" asked the man with the
black beard, with one hand behind him. "I guess it's
about time we saw him."

The window of the inn was suddenly smashed in, and
there was a screaming and running to and fro in the
street. The policeman had been standing on the settee
staring out, craning to see who was at the door. He got
down with raised eyebrows. "It's that," he said. The barman stood in front of the bar-parlour door which was
now locked on Mr. Marvel, stared at the smashed window, and came round to the two other men.

Everything was suddenly quiet. "I wish I had my truncheon," said the policeman, going irresolutely to the
door. "Once we open, in he comes. There's no stopping
him."

"Don't you be in too much hurry about that door," said
the anaemic cabman, anxiously.

"Draw the bolts," said the man with the black beard,
"and if he comes –" He showed a revolver in his
hand.

"That won't do," said the policeman; "that's murder."

"I know what country I'm in," said the man with the
beard. "I'm going to let off at his legs. Draw the
bolts."

"Not with that thing going off behind me," said the barman, craning over the blind.

---

8 **settee:** Couch, Sofa.
9 **to crane:** den Hals recken.
11 **bar-parlour:** Nebenzimmer (für private Unterhaltungen).
25 **to let off:** schießen, feuern.

"Very well," said the man with the black beard, and stooping down, revolver ready, drew them himself. Barman, cabman, and policeman faced about.

"Come in," said the bearded man in an undertone,
5 standing back and facing the unbolted doors with his pistol behind him. No one came in, the door remained closed. Five minutes afterwards when a second cabman pushed his head in cautiously, they were still waiting, and an anxious face peered out of the bar-parlour and
10 supplied information. "Are all the doors of the house shut?" asked Marvel. "He's going round – prowling round. He's as artful as the devil."

"Good Lord!" said the burly barman. "There's the back! Just watch them doors! I say! –" He looked about him
15 helplessly. The bar-parlour door slammed and they heard the key turn. "There's the yard door and the private door. The yard door —"

He rushed out of the bar.

In a minute he reappeared with a carving-knife in his
20 hand. "The yard door was open!" he said, and his fat underlip dropped. "He may be in the house now!" said the first cabman.

"He's not in the kitchen," said the barman. "There's two women there, and I've stabbed every inch of it with this
25 little beef slicer. And they don't think he's come in. They haven't noticed —"

---

3 **to face about:** (gespannt) zuschauen.
4 **in an undertone:** in gedämpftem Ton.
11f. **to prowl round:** herumschleichen, herumstreifen.
12 **artful:** listig, tückisch.
19 **carving-knife:** Tranchiermesser.
24 **to stab s.th.:** in etwas (hinein)stechen, (herum)stochern.
25 **beef slicer:** langes Fleischermesser.

"Have you fastened it?" asked the first cabman.

"I'm out of frocks," said the barman.

The man with the beard replaced his revolver. And even as he did so the flap of the bar was shut down and the bolt clicked, and then with a tremendous thud the catch of the door snapped and the bar-parlour door burst open. They heard Marvel squeal like a caught leveret, and forthwith they were clambering over the bar to his rescue. The bearded man's revolver cracked and the looking-glass at the back of the parlour was starred brightly and came smashing and tinkling down.

As the barman entered the room he saw Marvel, curiously crumpled up and struggling against the door that led to the yard and kitchen. The door flew open while the barman hesitated, and Marvel was dragged into the kitchen. There was a scream and a clatter of pans. Marvel, head down, and lugging back obstinately, was forced to the kitchen door, and the bolts were drawn.

Then the policeman, who had been trying to pass the barman, rushed in, followed by one of the cabmen, gripped the wrist of the invisible hand that collared Marvel, was hit in the face and went reeling back. The door

---

2 **I'm out of frocks:** (fig.) ich bin aus den Kinderkleidern heraus.

5 **catch:** Schließhaken; (Tür-)Schnapper.

7 **to squeal:** quietschen, hell schreien.

   leveret: junger Hase.

9 **to crack:** knallen.

10 **to be starred:** etwa: eine sternförmige Einschlagstelle aufweisen.

11 **to tinkle:** klirren.

13 **crumpled up:** zusammengekrümmt.

16 **clatter:** Geklapper; Geklirr.

17 **to lug:** zerren; sich sträuben.

   obstinately (adv.): hartnäckig.

21 **to collar:** schnappen, packen.

opened, and Marvel made a frantic effort to obtain a
lodgment behind it. Then the cabman clutched something. "I got him," said the cabman. The barman's red
hands came clawing at the unseen. "Here he is!" said the
5 barman.

Mr. Marvel, released, suddenly dropped to the ground
and made an attempt to crawl behind the legs of the fighting men. The struggle blundered round the edge of the
door. The voice of the Invisible Man was heard for the
10 first time, yelling out sharply, as the policeman trod on his
foot. Then he cried out passionately and his fists flew
round like flails. The cabman suddenly whooped and
doubled up, kicked under the diaphragm. The door into
the bar-parlour from the kitchen slammed and covered
15 Mr. Marvel's retreat. The men in the kitchen found themselves clutching at and struggling with empty air.

"Where's he gone?" cried the man with the beard.
"Out?"

"This way," said the policeman, stepping into the yard
20 and stopping.

A piece of tile whizzed by his head and smashed among
the crockery on the kitchen table.

"I'll show him," shouted the man with the black beard,
and suddenly a steel barrel shone over the policeman's

---

2 **lodgment:** Verschanzung, Schutz.
4 **to claw at s.th.:** sich an etwas krallen.
8 **to blunder:** hier: sich ungeordnet bewegen.
12 **flail:** Dreschflegel.
   to whoop: aufheulen.
13 **to double up:** sich krümmen.
   diaphragm: Zwerchfell.
21 **to whizz:** (vorbei)zischen, -sausen.
22 **crockery:** Geschirr.
24 **steel barrel:** stählerner Lauf (einer Schußwaffe).

shoulder, and five bullets had followed one another into
the twilight whence the missile had come. As he fired,
the man with the beard moved his hand in a horizontal
curve, so that his shots radiated out into the narrow yard
5 like spokes from a wheel.

A silence followed. "Five cartridges," said the man with
the black beard. "That's the best of all. Four aces and the
joker. Get a lantern, someone, and come and feel about
9 for his body."

Chapter XVII

Doctor Kemp's Visitor

Doctor Kemp had continued writing in his study until
the shots aroused him. Crack, crack, crack, they came
one after the other.

15 "Hullo!" said Doctor Kemp, putting his pen into his
mouth again and listening. "Who's letting off revolvers
in Burdock? What are the asses at now?"

He went to the south window, threw it up, and leaning
out stared down on the network of windows, beaded

---

1 **bullet:** (Gewehr-)Kugel.
2 **whence** (arch.): von wo, woher.
4 **to radiate out:** (fig.) ausstrahlen, strahlenförmig ausgehen, sich
 strahlenförmig verbreiten.
5 **spoke:** Speiche.
6 **cartridge:** Patrone.
7 **ace:** As (Spielkarte).
19 **beaded:** wie auf einer Perlenkette aufgereiht.

gas-lamps and shops with black interstices of roof and
yard that made up the town at night. "Looks like a crowd
down the hill," he said, "by the Cricketers," and remained watching. Thence his eyes wandered over the
5 town to far away where the ships' lights shone, and the
pier glowed, a little illuminated pavilion like a gem of
yellow light. The moon in its first quarter hung over the
western hill, and the stars were clear and almost tropi-
cally bright.

10 After five minutes, during which his mind had travelled
into a remote speculation of social conditions of the future, and lost itself at last over the time dimension, Doctor Kemp roused himself with a sigh, pulled down the
window again, and returned to his writing-desk.

15 It must have been about an hour after this that the front-
door bell rang. He had been writing slackly and with
intervals of abstraction, since the shots. He sat listening.
He heard the servant answer the door, and waited for
her feet on the staircase, but she did not come. "Wonder
20 what that was," said Doctor Kemp.

He tried to resume his work, failed, got up, went downstairs from his study to the landing, rang, and called over
the balustrade to the housemaid as she appeared in the
hall below. "Was that a letter?" he asked.

25 "Only a runaway ring, sir," she answered.

"I'm restless to-night," he said to himself. He went back

---

1 **interstice:** Lücke.
6 **pier:** Landungsbrücke.
  illuminated: erleuchtet.
  gem: Edelstein.
16 **slackly** (adv.): nachlässig, unkonzentriert.
17 **abstraction:** Geistesabwesenheit.
25 **runaway ring:** blindes Läuten.

to his study, and this time attacked his work resolutely.
In a little while he was hard at work again, and the only
sounds in the room were the ticking of the clock and the
subdued shrillness of his quill, hurrying in the very
5 centre of the circle of light his lamp-shade threw on his
table.

It was two o'clock before Doctor Kemp had finished his
work for the night. He rose, yawned, and went downstairs to bed. He had already removed his coat and vest,
10 when he noticed that he was thirsty. He took a candle
and went down to the dining-room in search of a syphon
and whiskey.

Doctor Kemp's scientific pursuits had made him a very
observant man, and as he recrossed the hall, he noticed
15 a dark spot on the linoleum near the mat at the foot of
the stairs. He went on upstairs, and then it suddenly occurred to him to ask himself what the spot on the linoleum might be. Apparently some sub-conscious element
was at work. At any rate, he turned with his burden,
20 went back to the hall, put down the syphon and whiskey,
and bending down, touched the spot. Without any great
surprise he found it had the stickiness and colour of drying blood.

He took up his burden again, and returned upstairs,

---

4 **subdued:** leise, gedämpft.
   shrillness: hier: (helles) Kratzgeräusch.
   quill: Feder(kiel).
9 **vest:** Weste.
11 **syphon:** Siphon(flasche) (Gefäß, aus dem beim Öffnen die einge-
   schlossene Kohlensäure das Mineralwasser o. ä. herausdrückt).
13 **pursuits:** Studien.
14 **observant:** aufmerksam.
18 **sub-conscious:** unterbewußt.
19 **burden:** gemeint sind die Flaschen.

looking about him and trying to account for the blood-
spot. On the landing he saw something and stopped
astonished. The door-handle of his own room was blood-
stained.

5 He looked at his own hand. It was quite clean, and then
he remembered that the door of his room had been
open when he came down from his study, and that consequently he had not touched the handle at all. He
went straight into his room, his face quite calm – per-
10 haps a trifle more resolute than usual. His glance, wandering inquisitively, fell on the bed. On the counterpane was a mess of blood, and the sheet had been torn.
He had not noticed this before because he had walked
straight to the dressing-table. On the further side the
15 bed-clothes were depressed as if someone had been recently sitting there.
Then he had an odd impression that he had heard a loud
voice say, "Good Heavens! – *Kemp!*" But Doctor Kemp
was no believer in Voices.
20 He stood staring at the tumbled sheets. Was that really a
voice? He looked about again, but noticed nothing further than the disordered and blood-stained bed. Then he
distinctly heard a movement across the room, near the
wash-hand stand. All men, however highly educated, re-
25 tain some superstitious inklings. The feeling that is

7f. **consequently** (adv.): folglich.
10 **a trifle**: ein wenig.
11 **inquisitively** (adv.): neugierig, forschend.
11f. **counterpane**: Bettdecke.
12 **mess**: Schlamassel; Schmutz, Durcheinander.
14 **dressing-table**: Frisierkommode.
20 **tumbled**: zerwühlt.
24 **wash-hand stand**: Waschtisch.
25 **superstitious**: abergläubisch.

called "eerie" came upon him. He closed the door of the
room, came forward to the dressing-table, and put down
his burdens. Suddenly, with a start, he perceived a coiled
and blood-stained bandage of linen rag hanging in mid-
5 air, between him and the wash-hand stand.
He stared at this in amazement. It was an empty bandage, a bandage properly tied but quite empty. He would
have advanced to grasp it, but a touch arrested him, and
a voice speaking quite close to him.
10 "Kemp!" said the Voice.
"Eigh?" said Kemp, with his mouth open.
"Keep your nerve," said the Voice. "I'm an Invisible
Man."
Kemp made no answer for a space, simply stared at the
15 bandage. "Invisible Man," he said.
"I'm an Invisible Man," repeated the Voice.
The story he had been active to ridicule only that morning rushed through Kemp's brain. He does not appear to
have been either very much frightened or very greatly
20 surprised at the moment. Realisation came later.
"I thought it was all a lie," he said. The thought uppermost in his mind was the reiterated arguments of the
morning. "Have you a bandage on?" he asked.
"Yes," said the Invisible Man.
25 "Oh!" said Kemp, and then roused himself. "I say!" he
said. "But this is nonsense. It's some trick." He stepped
forward suddenly, and his hand, extended towards the
bandage, met invisible fingers.

---

1 **eerie:** unheimlich, schaurig.
3 **coiled:** zu einer Spirale gedreht.
17 **to ridicule s.th.:** etwas ins Lächerliche ziehen.
22 **to reiterate:** (dauernd) wiederholen.

He recoiled at the touch and his colour changed.

"Keep steady, Kemp, for God's sake! I want help badly.
Stop!"

The hand gripped his arm. He struck at it.

5 "Kemp!" cried the Voice. "Kemp! Keep steady!" and
the grip tightened.

A frantic desire to free himself took possession of
Kemp. The hand of the bandaged arm gripped his shoulder, and he was suddenly tripped and flung backwards
10 upon the bed. He opened his mouth to shout, and the
corner of the sheet was thrust between his teeth. The Invisible Man had him down grimly, but his arms were free
and he struck and tried to kick savagely.

"Listen to reason, will you?" said the Invisible Man,
15 sticking to him in spite of a pounding in the ribs. "By
Heaven! you'll madden me in a minute!

Lie still, you fool!" bawled the Invisible Man in Kemp's
ear.

Kemp struggled for another moment and then lay
20 still.

"If you shout I'll smash your face," said the Invisible
Man, relieving his mouth.

"I'm an Invisible Man. It's no foolishness, and no magic.
I really am an Invisible Man. And I want your help. I
25 don't want to hurt you, but if you behave like a frantic
rustic, I must. Don't you remember me, Kemp? – Griffin, of University College?"

"Let me get up," said Kemp. "I'll stop where I am. And
let me sit quiet for a minute."

---

1 **to recoil at s.th.:** entsetzt vor etwas zurückfahren.
15 **to pound:** schlagen, stoßen.
22 **to relieve:** frei machen, befreien.
26 **rustic:** Bauerntölpel.

He sat up and felt his neck.

"I am Griffin, of University College, and I have made myself invisible. I am just an ordinary man – a man you have known – made invisible."

"Griffin?" said Kemp.

"Griffin," answered the Voice, –"a younger student, almost an albino, six feet high, and broad, with a pink and white face and red eyes, – who won the medal for chemistry."

"I am confused," said Kemp. "My brain is rioting. What has this to do with Griffin?"

"I *am* Griffin."

Kemp thought. "It's horrible," he said. "But what devilry must happen to make a man invisible?"

"It's no devilry. It's a process, sane and intelligible enough —"

"It's horrible!" said Kemp. "How on earth —?"

"It's horrible enough. But I'm wounded and in pain, and tired – Great God! Kemp, you are a man. Take it steady. Give me some food and drink, and let me sit down here."

Kemp stared at the bandage as it moved across the room, then saw a basket chair dragged across the floor and come to rest near the bed. It creaked, and the seat was depressed the quarter of an inch or so. He rubbed his eyes and felt his neck again. "This beats ghosts," he said, and laughed stupidly.

---

7 **albino:** Mensch mit fehlender Farbstoffbildung.
10 **to riot:** hier (fig.): sich drehen, durcheinander sein.
15 **devilry:** Teufelei, Teufelsspuk.
   sane: normal, vernünftig.
   intelligible: verständlich.
19 **take it steady:** fassen Sie sich!

"That's better. Thank Heaven, you're getting sensible!"

"Or silly," said Kemp, and knuckled his eyes.

"Give me some whiskey. I'm near dead."

5 "It didn't feel so. Where are you? If I get up shall I run into you? *There!* all right. Whiskey? Here. Where shall I give it you?"

The chair creaked and Kemp felt the glass drawn away from him. He let go by an effort; his instinct was all
10 against it. It came to rest poised twenty inches above the front edge of the seat of the chair. He stared at it in infinite perplexity. "This is – this *must* be – hypnotism. You must have suggested you are invisible."

"Nonsense," said the Voice.

15 "It's frantic."

"Listen to me."

"I demonstrated conclusively this morning," began Kemp, "that invisibility —"

"Never mind what you've demonstrated! – I'm starv-
20 ing," said the Voice, "and the night is – chilly to a man without clothes."

"Food!" said Kemp.

The tumbler of whiskey tilted itself. "Yes," said the Invisible Man rapping it down. "Have you got a dressing-
25 gown?"

Kemp made some exclamation in an undertone. He walked to a wardrobe and produced a robe of dingy

3 **to knuckle one's eyes:** sich mit den Fingerknöcheln die Augen reiben.
10 **poised:** in der Luft schwebend.
17 **conclusively** (adv.): schlüssig.
23 **tumbler:** (Whiskey-)Glas.
   to tilt o.s.: sich neigen, kippen.
27 **dingy:** schmuddelig.

scarlet. "This do?" he asked. It was taken from him. It hung limp for a moment in mid-air, fluttered weirdly, stood full and decorous buttoning itself, and sat down in his chair. "Drawers, socks, slippers would be a comfort," said the Unseen, curtly. "And food."

"Anything. But this is the insanest thing I ever was in, in my life!"

He turned out his drawers for the articles, and then went downstairs to ransack his larder. He came back with some cold cutlets and bread, pulled up a light table, and placed them before his guest. "Never mind knives," said his visitor, and a cutlet hung in mid-air, with a sound of gnawing.

"Invisible!" said Kemp, and sat down on a bedroom chair.

"I always like to get something about me before I eat," said the Invisible Man, with a full mouth, eating greedily. "Queer fancy!"

"I suppose that wrist is all right," said Kemp.

"Trust me," said the Invisible Man.

"Of *all* the strange and wonderful —"

"Exactly. But it's odd I should blunder into *your* house to get my bandaging. My first stroke of luck! Anyhow I meant to sleep in this house to-night. You must stand

---

1 **this do?:** reicht das?
2 **weirdly** (adv.): geisterhaft, unheimlich.
3 **decorous:** gesittet.
4 **drawers:** Unterhose(n).
5 **curtly** (adv.): kurz, knapp, barsch.
9 **to ransack:** plündern.
   larder: Speisekammer.
11 **Never mind knives:** Messer sind nicht nötig.
18 **queer fancy:** (das ist so eine) seltsame Laune.
22 **to blunder into s.th.:** zufällig in etwas hineingeraten, hineinstolpern.

that! It's a filthy nuisance, my blood showing, isn't it?
Quite a clot over there. Gets visible as it coagulates,
I see. I've been in the house three hours."

"But how's it done?" began Kemp, in a tone of exasperation. "Confound it! The whole business – it's unreasonable from beginning to end."

"Quite reasonable," said the Invisible Man. "Perfectly
reasonable."

He reached over and secured the whiskey bottle. Kemp
stared at the devouring dressing-gown. A ray of candle-
light penetrating a torn patch in the right shoulder, made
a triangle of light under the left ribs. "What were the
shots?" he asked. "How did the shooting begin?"

"There was a fool of a man – a sort of confederate of
mine – curse him! – who tried to steal my money. *Has*
done so."

"Is *he* invisible too?"

"No."

"Well?"

"Can't I have some more to eat before I tell you all
that? I'm hungry – in pain. And you want me to tell
stories!"

Kemp got up. "*You* didn't do any shooting?" he asked.

"Not me," said his visitor. "Some fool I'd never seen
fired at random. A lot of them got scared. They all got

---

 1 **filthy** (infml.): verflucht, ekelhaft.
 2 **clot:** geronnenes Blut.
   to coagulate: gerinnen.
 9 **to secure:** sichern, sicherstellen.
10 **to devour:** gierig essen, verschlingen.
11 **torn patch:** Riß.
12 **triangle:** Dreieck.
14 **confederate:** Verbündeter.

scared at me. Curse them! – I say – I want more to eat
than this, Kemp."

"I'll see what there is more to eat downstairs," said
Kemp. "Not much, I'm afraid."

After he had done eating, and he made a heavy meal, the
Invisible Man demanded a cigar. He bit the end savagely
before Kemp could find a knife, and cursed when the
outer leaf loosened. It was strange to see him smoking;
his mouth and throat, pharynx and nares, became visible
as a sort of whirling smoke cast.

"This blessed gift of smoking!" he said, and puffed vig-
orously. "I'm lucky to have fallen upon you, Kemp.
You must help me. Fancy tumbling on you just now!
I'm in a devilish scrape. I've been mad, I think. The
things I have been through! But we will do things yet.
Let me tell you —"

He helped himself to more whiskey and soda. Kemp
got up, looked about him, and fetched himself a glass
from his spare room. "It's wild – but I suppose I may
drink."

"You haven't changed much, Kemp, these dozen years.
You fair men don't. Cool and methodical – after the first
collapse. I must tell you. We will work together!"

"But how was it all done?" said Kemp, "and how did you
get like this?"

---

9 **pharynx:** Rachen.
  nares (Lat., pl.): Nase, Nasenhöhle.
10 **smoke cast:** Form aus Rauch.
11 f. **vigorously** (adv.): kräftig.
12 **to fall upon s.o.:** auf jdn. stoßen, jdm. begegnen.
13 **to tumble on s.o.:** hier: zufällig auf jdn. stoßen.
14 **scrape:** (fig.) Klemme.

"For God's sake, let me smoke in peace for a little while! And then I will begin to tell you."

But the story was not told that night. The Invisible Man's wrist was growing painful, he was feverish, exhausted, and his mind came round to brood upon his chase down the hill and the struggle about the inn. He spoke in fragments of Marvel, he smoked faster, his voice grew angry. Kemp tried to gather what he could.

"He was afraid of me, I could see he was afraid of me," said the Invisible Man many times over. "He meant to give me the slip – he was always casting about! What a fool I was!

The cur!

I should have killed him —"

"Where did you get the money?" asked Kemp, abruptly.

The Invisible Man was silent for a space. "I can't tell you to-night," he said.

He groaned suddenly and leant forward, supporting his invisible head on invisible hands. "Kemp," he said, "I've had no sleep for near three days, – except a couple of dozes of an hour or so. I must sleep soon."

"Well, have my room – have this room."

"But how can I sleep? If I sleep – he will get away. Ugh! What does it matter?"

"What's the shot-wound?" asked Kemp, abruptly.

"Nothing – scratch and blood. Oh, God! How I want sleep!"

---

5 **to brood upon s.th.:** über etwas nachbrüten.

11 **to cast about:** sich (nach etwas) umsehen; hier: sich (nach einer Fluchtmöglichkeit) umsehen.

22 **doze:** Nickerchen.

"Why not?"

The Invisible Man appeared to be regarding Kemp. "Because I've a particular objection to being caught by my fellow-men," he said slowly.

Kemp started.

"Fool that I am!" said the Invisible Man, striking the table smartly. "I've put the idea into your head."

Chapter XVIII

The Invisible Man Sleeps

Exhausted and wounded as the Invisible Man was, he refused to accept Kemp's word that his freedom should be respected. He examined the two windows of the bedroom, drew up the blinds, and opened the sashes, to confirm Kemp's statement that a retreat by them would be possible. Outside the night was very quiet and still, and the new moon was setting over the down. Then he examined the keys of the bedroom and the two dressing-room doors, to satisfy himself that these also could be made an assurance of freedom. Finally he expressed himself satisfied. He stood on the hearth-rug and Kemp heard the sound of a yawn.

"I'm sorry," said the Invisible Man, "if I cannot tell you all that I have done to-night. But I am worn out. It's grotesque, no doubt. It's horrible! But believe me, Kemp, it

7 **smartly** (adv.): hart.
13 **sash**: Schiebefenster.
23 **worn out**: erschöpft.

is quite a possible thing. I have made a discovery. I meant to keep it to myself. I can't. I must have a partner. And you – We can do such things – But to-morrow. Now, Kemp, I feel as though I must sleep or perish."

5 Kemp stood in the middle of the room staring at the headless garment. "I suppose I must leave you," he said. "It's – incredible. Three things happening like this, overturning all my preconceptions, would make me insane. But it's real! Is there anything more that I can get you?"

10 "Only bid me good-night," said Griffin.

"Good-night," said Kemp, and shook an invisible hand. He walked sideways to the door. Suddenly the dressing-gown walked quickly towards him. "Understand me!" said the dressing-gown. "No attempts to hamper me, or

15 capture me! Or —"

Kemp's face changed a little. "I thought I gave you my word," he said.

Kemp closed the door softly behind him, and the key was turned upon him forthwith. Then, as he stood with

20 an expression of passive amazement on his face, the rapid feet came to the door of the dressing-room and that too was locked. Kemp slapped his brow with his hand. "Am I dreaming? Has the world gone mad – or have I?"

25 He laughed, and put his hand to the locked door. "Barred out of my own bedroom, by a flagrant absurdity!" he said.

---

4 **to perish:** sterben.
8 **preconception:** feste Vorstellung, vorgefaßte Meinung.
10 **to bid s.o. good-night:** jdm. gute Nacht wünschen.
14 **to hamper s.o.:** jdn. behindern, jdm. Schwierigkeiten bereiten.
15 **to capture:** ergreifen, festnehmen.
26 **flagrant:** himmelschreiend.

He walked to the head of the staircase, turned, and stared at the locked doors. "It's fact," he said. He put his fingers to his slightly bruised neck. "Undeniable fact! But —"

He shook his head hopelessly, turned, and went downstairs.

He lit the dining-room lamp, got out a cigar, and began pacing the room, ejaculating. Now and then he would argue with himself.

"Invisible!" he said.

"Is there such a thing as an invisible animal? In the sea, yes. Thousands! millions! All the larvae, all the little nauplii and tornarias, all the microscopic things, the jelly-fish. In the sea there are more things invisible than visible! I never thought of that before. And in the ponds too! All those little pond-life things, – specks of colourless translucent jelly! But in air? No!

It can't be.

But after all – why not?

If a man was made of glass he would still be visible."

His meditation became profound. The bulk of three cigars had passed into the invisible or diffused as a white ash over the carpet before he spoke again. Then it was

---

8 **to ejaculate:** Worte ausstoßen.

12 **larva** (Lat., pl. *larvae*): Larve.

13 **nauplius** (Lat., pl. *nauplii*): Larvenform der Ruderfuß-, Rankenfuß- und einiger Muschelkrebse.

   tornaria (Lat.): im Flachwasser der Gezeiten schwimmende Larve der Eichelwürmer.

14 **jelly-fish:** Qualle.

17 **translucent:** lichtdurchlässig.

21 **meditation:** Nachdenken.

   profound: tiefgründig.

22 **to diffuse:** sich ausbreiten.

merely an exclamation. He turned aside, walked out of
the room, and went into his little consulting-room and lit
the gas there. It was a little room, because Doctor Kemp
did not live by practice, and in it were the day's newspa-
5 pers. The morning's paper lay carelessly opened and
thrown aside. He caught it up, turned it over, and read
the account of a "Strange Story from Iping" that the
mariner at Port Stowe had spelt over so painfully to Mr.
Marvel. Kemp read it swiftly.

10 "Wrapped up!" said Kemp. "Disguised! Hiding it! 'No
one seems to have been aware of his misfortune.' What
the devil *is* his game?"
He dropped the paper, and his eye went seeking. "Ah!"
he said, and caught up the "St. James's Gazette," lying
15 folded up as it arrived. "Now we shall get at the truth,"
said Doctor Kemp. He rent the paper open; a couple of
columns confronted him. "An Entire Village in Sussex
goes Mad" was the heading.
"Good Heavens!" said Kemp, reading eagerly an in-
20 credulous account of the events in Iping, on the previous
afternoon, that have already been described. Over the
leaf the report in the morning paper had been reprinted.
He re-read it. "Ran through the streets striking right and
left. Jaffers insensible. Mr. Huxter in great pain – still un-
25 able to describe what he saw. Painful humiliation – vicar.
Woman ill with terror! Windows smashed. This extraor-

---

2 **consulting-room:** Sprechzimmer.
4 **practice:** Arztpraxis.
8 **to spell s.th. over:** etwas vorbuchstabieren.
17 **column:** (Druck-)Spalte.
19f. **incredulous:** unglaublich.
24 **insensible:** besinnungslos.
25 **humiliation:** Demütigung.

dinary story probably a fabrication. Too good not to print – *cum grano!*"

He dropped the paper and stared blankly in front of him. "Probably a fabrication!"

5 He caught up the paper again, and re-read the whole business. "But when does the Tramp come in? Why the deuce was he chasing a Tramp?"

He sat down abruptly on the surgical couch. "He's not only invisible," he said, "but he's mad! Homicidal!"

10 When dawn came to mingle its pallor with the lamp-light and cigar smoke of the dining-room, Kemp was still pacing up and down, trying to grasp the incredible.

He was altogether too excited to sleep. His servants, descending sleepily, discovered him, and were inclined to

15 think that over-study had worked this ill on him. He gave them extraordinary but quite explicit instructions to lay breakfast for two in the belvedere study – and then to confine themselves to the basement and ground-floor. Then he continued to pace the dining-room until the

20 morning's paper came. That had much to say and little to tell, beyond the confirmation of the evening before and a very baldly written account of another remarkable tale

---

1 **fabrication:** Lügengeschichte, ‚Ente'.
2 **cum grano!** (Lat.): *cum grano salis:* mit einem Körnchen Salz, d. h. nicht ganz wörtlich zu nehmen.
8 **surgical couch:** Behandlungscouch.
9 **homicidal:** gemeingefährlich, mordlustig.
10 **pallor:** Blässe; hier: fahles Licht.
15 **to work s.th. on s.o.:** etwas bei jdm. bewirken, anrichten.
16 **explicit:** unmißverständlich, deutlich.
18 **to confine o.s. to s.th.:** sich auf etwas beschränken, sich nur in etwas aufhalten.
   basement: Kellergeschoß.
22 **baldly** (adv.): einfach, schlicht.

from Port Burdock. This gave Kemp the essence of the
happenings at the Jolly Cricketers, and the name of
Marvel. "He has made me keep with him twenty-four
hours," Marvel testified. Certain minor facts were added
5 to the Iping story, notably the cutting of the village tele-
graph-wire. But there was nothing to throw light on the
connexion between the Invisible Man and the Tramp;
for Mr. Marvel had supplied no information about the
three books, or the money with which he was lined. The
10 incredulous tone had vanished and a shoal of reporters
and inquirers were already at work elaborating the matter.
Kemp read every scrap of the report and sent his housemaid out to get every one of the morning papers she
15 could. These also he devoured.
"He is invisible!" he said. "And it reads like rage growing to mania! The things he may do! The things he may
do! And he's upstairs free as the air. What on earth
ought I to do?
20 For instance, would it be a breach of faith if –? No."
He went to a little untidy desk in the corner, and began
a note. He tore this up half written, and wrote another.
He read it over and considered it. Then he took an enve-
lope and addressed it to "Colonel Adye, Port Burdock."
25 The Invisible Man awoke even as Kemp was doing this.
He awoke in an evil temper, and Kemp, alert for every

---

1 **essence:** das Wesentliche.
4 **minor:** von geringerer Bedeutung.
9 **to be lined:** etwa: reichlich ausgestattet sein (vgl. *to line one's pockets:*
   sich die Taschen füllen).
10 **shoal:** Schwarm, Schar.
17 **mania:** Manie, Wahnsinn.
20 **breach of faith:** Treue-, Wortbruch.
26 **alert:** gespannt, aufmerksam.

sound, heard his pattering feet rush suddenly across the bedroom overhead. Then a chair was flung over and the wash-hand stand tumbler smashed. Kemp hurried upstairs and rapped eagerly.

Chapter XIX

Certain First Principles

"What's the matter?" asked Kemp, when the Invisible Man admitted him.

"Nothing," was the answer.

"But, confound it! The smash?"

"Fit of temper," said the Invisible Man. "Forgot this arm; and it's sore."

"You're rather liable to that sort of thing."

"I am."

Kemp walked across the room and picked up the fragments of broken glass. "All the facts are out about you," said Kemp, standing up with the glass in his hand; "all that happened in Iping, and down the hill. The world has become aware of its invisible citizen. But no one knows you are here."

The Invisible Man swore.

"The secret's out. I gather it was a secret. I don't know

---

1 **to patter:** trappeln.
11 **fit of temper:** Anfall von schlechter Laune.
13 **to be liable to s.th.:** anfällig für etwas sein, zu etwas neigen.
16 **to be out:** bekannt werden, an den Tag kommen.

what your plans are, but of course I'm anxious to help you."

The Invisible Man sat down on the bed.

"There's breakfast upstairs," said Kemp, speaking as easily as possible, and he was delighted to find his strange guest rose willingly. Kemp led the way up the narrow staircase to the belvedere.

"Before we can do anything else," said Kemp, "I must understand a little more about this invisibility of yours."

He had sat down, after one nervous glance out of the window, with the air of a man who has talking to do. His doubts of the sanity of the entire business flashed and vanished again as he looked across to where Griffin sat at the breakfast-table, – a headless, handless dressing-gown, wiping unseen lips on a miraculously held serviette.

"It's simple enough – and credible enough," said Griffin, putting the serviette aside and leaning the invisible head on an invisible hand.

"No doubt, to you, but –" Kemp laughed.

"Well, yes; to me it seemed wonderful at first, no doubt. But now, great God! – But we will do great things yet! I came on the stuff first at Chesilstowe."

"Chesilstowe?"

"I went there after I left London. You know I dropped medicine and took up physics? No? – well, I did. Light – fascinated me."

"Ah!"

"Optical density! The whole subject is a network of rid-

---

12 **sanity:** Vernünftigkeit, Glaubwürdigkeit.
29 **density:** Dichte.

dles – a network with solutions glimmering elusively through. And being but two and twenty and full of enthusiasm, I said, 'I will devote my life to this. This is worth while.' You know what fools we are at two and twenty?"

"Fools then or fools now," said Kemp.

"As though Knowing could be any satisfaction to a man! But I went to work – like a nigger. And I had hardly worked and thought about the matter six months before light came through one of the meshes suddenly – blindingly! I found a general principle of pigments and refraction, – a formula, a geometrical expression involving four dimensions. Fools, common men, even common mathematicians, do not know anything of what some general expression may mean to the student of molecular physics. In the books – the books that Tramp has hidden – there are marvels, miracles! But this was not a method, it was an idea that might lead to a method by which it would be possible, without changing any other property of matter, – except, in some instances, colours, – to lower the refractive index of a substance, solid or liquid, to that of air – so far as all practical purposes are concerned."

"Phew!" said Kemp. "That's odd! But still I don't see quite – I can understand that thereby you could spoil a valuable stone, but personal invisibility is a far cry."

---

 1 **to glimmer:** (fig.) schimmern.
    elusively (adv.): trügerisch, schwer faßbar.
 9 **mesh:** Masche.
10 f. **refraction:** (Strahlen-)Brechung.
14 f. **molecular:** molekular, die Moleküle betreffend.
19 **property of matter:** Eigenschaft der Materie.
20 **refractive index:** Brechungsindex.
25 **to be a far cry** (fig.): etwas ganz anderes sein.

"Precisely," said Griffin. "But consider: Visibility depends on the action of the visible bodies on light. Either a body absorbs light, or it reflects or refracts it, or does all these things. If it neither reflects nor refracts nor absorbs light, it cannot of itself be visible. You see an opaque red box, for instance, because the colour absorbs some of the light and reflects the rest, all the red part of the light, to you. If it did not absorb any particular part of the light, but reflected it all, then it would be a shining white box. Silver! A diamond box would neither absorb much of the light nor reflect much from the general surface, but just here and there where the surfaces were favourable the light would be reflected and refracted, so that you would get a brilliant appearance of flashing reflections and translucencies, – a sort of skeleton of light. A glass box would not be so brilliant, not so clearly visible, as a diamond box, because there would be less refraction and reflection. See that? From certain points of view you would see quite clearly through it. Some kinds of glass would be more visible than others, a box of flint glass would be brighter than a box of ordinary window glass. A box of very thin common glass would be hard to see in a bad light, because it would absorb hardly any light and refract and reflect very little. And if you put a sheet of common white glass in water, still more if you put it in some denser liquid than water, it would vanish almost altogether, because light passing from water to glass is only slightly refracted or reflected or indeed af-

---

6 **opaque:** undurchsichtig.
15 **translucency:** Lichtdurchlässigkeit.
20f. **flint glass:** Kristallglas.
28f. **to affect s.th.:** etwas beeinflussen, auf etwas einwirken.

fected in any way. It is almost as invisible as a jet of coal
gas or hydrogen is in air. And for precisely the same reason!"

"Yes," said Kemp, "that is pretty plain sailing."

5 "And here is another fact you will know to be true. If a
sheet of glass is smashed, Kemp, and beaten into a powder, it becomes much more visible while it is in the air; it
becomes at last an opaque white powder. This is because
the powdering multiplies the surfaces of the glass at
10 which refraction and reflection occur. In the sheet of
glass there are only two surfaces; in the powder the light
is reflected or refracted by each grain it passes through,
and very little gets right through the powder. But if the
white powdered glass is put into water, it forthwith van-
15 ishes. The powdered glass and water have much the
same refractive index; that is, the light undergoes very
little refraction or reflection in passing from one to the
other.

You make the glass invisible by putting it into a liquid of
20 nearly the same refractive index; a transparent thing becomes invisible if it is put in any medium of almost the
same refractive index. And if you will consider only a
second, you will see also that the powder of glass might
be made to vanish in air, if its refractive index could be
25 made the same as that of air; for then there would be no
refraction or reflection as the light passed from glass to
air."

"Yes, yes," said Kemp. "But a man's not powdered
glass!"

---

1 f. **coal gas:** Leuchtgas.
2 **hydrogen:** Wasserstoff.
4 **that is pretty plain sailing** (infml.): das ist ganz einfach.

"No," said Griffin. "He's more transparent!"

"Nonsense!"

"That from a doctor! How one forgets! Have you already forgotten your physics, in ten years? Just think of
5 all the things that are transparent and seem not to be so. Paper, for instance, is made up of transparent fibres, and it is white and opaque only for the same reason that a powder of glass is white and opaque. Oil white paper, fill up the interstices between the particles with oil so that
10 there is no longer refraction or reflection except at the surfaces, and it becomes as transparent as glass. And not only paper, but cotton fibre, linen fibre, wool fibre, woody fibre, and *bone*, Kemp, *flesh*, Kemp, *hair*, Kemp, *nails* and *nerves*, Kemp, in fact the whole fabric of a man
15 except the red of his blood and the black pigment of hair, are all made up of transparent, colourless tissue. So little suffices to make us visible one to the other. For the most part the fibres of a living creature are no more opaque than water."

20 "Great Heavens!" cried Kemp. "Of course, of course! I was thinking only last night of the sea larvae and all jellyfish!"

"*Now* you have me! And all that I knew and had in mind a year after I left London – six years ago. But I kept it to
25 myself. I had to do my work under frightful disadvantages. Oliver, my professor, was a scientific bounder, a journalist by instinct, a thief of ideas, – he was always

6 **fibre:** Faser.
14 **fabric:** Struktur.
16 **tissue:** Gewebe.
17 **to suffice:** genügen.
26 **bounder** (BE, slang, arch.): Schurke.

prying! And you know the knavish system of the scientific world. I simply would not publish, and let him share my credit. I went on working, I got nearer and nearer making my formula into an experiment, a reality. I told no living soul, because I meant to flash my work upon the world with crushing effect, – to become famous at a blow. I took up the question of pigments to fill up certain gaps. And suddenly, not by design but by accident, I made a discovery in physiology."

"Yes?"

"You know the red colouring matter of blood; it can be made white – colourless – and remain with all the functions it has now!"

Kemp gave a cry of incredulous amazement.

The Invisible Man rose and began pacing the little study. "You may well exclaim. I remember that night. It was late at night, – in the daytime one was bothered with the gaping, silly students, – and I worked then sometimes till dawn. It came suddenly, splendid and complete into my mind. I was alone; the laboratory was still, with the tall lights burning brightly and silently. In all my great moments I have been alone. 'One could make an animal – a tissue – transparent! One could make it invisible! All except the pigments. I could be invisible!' I said, suddenly realising what it meant to be an albino with such knowledge. It was overwhelming. I left the filtering I was

---

1 **knavish** (arch.): schurkisch.
3 **credit:** hier: wissenschaftlicher Erfolg.
6 **crushing:** (fig.) überwältigend.
8 **by design:** absichtlich, geplant.
9 **physiology:** Lehre von den normalen Lebensvorgängen.
26 **overwhelming:** überwältigend.
    filtering: Filtrieren.

doing, and went and stared out of the great window at
the stars. 'I could be invisible!' I repeated.
To do such a thing would be to transcend magic. And I
beheld, unclouded by doubt, a magnificent vision of all
5 that invisibility might mean to a man, – the mystery, the
power, the freedom. Drawbacks I saw none. You have
only to think! And I, a shabby, poverty-struck, hemmed-
in demonstrator, teaching fools in a provincial college,
might suddenly become – this. I ask you, Kemp, if *you* –
10 Anyone, I tell you, would have flung himself upon that
research. And I worked three years, and every mountain
of difficulty I toiled over showed another from its summit. The infinite details! And the exasperation, – a professor, a provincial professor, always prying. 'When are
15 you going to publish this work of yours?' was his everlasting question. And the students, the cramped means!
Three years I had of it —
And after three years of secrecy and exasperation, I
found that to complete it was impossible, – impossible."
20 "How?" asked Kemp.
"Money," said the Invisible Man, and went again to stare
out of the window.
He turned round abruptly. "I robbed the old man –
robbed my father.
25 The money was not his, and he shot himself."

---

4 **unclouded:** (fig.) ungetrübt.
   magnificent: großartig.
6 **drawback:** Nachteil.
7f. **hemmed-in:** (fig.) eingeengt.
12 **to toil over s.th.:** etwas durch mühsame Arbeit bezwingen.
12f. **summit:** Gipfel.
15f. **everlasting:** fortwährend, ewig.
16 **cramped means:** beschränkte Mittel.

Chapter XX

At the House in Great Portland Street

For a moment Kemp sat in silence, staring at the back of the headless figure at the window. Then he started, struck by a thought, rose, took the Invisible Man's arm, and turned him away from the outlook.

"You are tired," he said, "and while I sit, you walk about. Have my chair."

He placed himself between Griffin and the nearest window.

For a space Griffin sat silent, and then he resumed abruptly: —

"I had left the Chesilstowe cottage already," he said, "when that happened. It was last December. I had taken a room in London, a large unfurnished room in a big ill-managed lodging-house in a slum near Great Portland Street. The room was soon full of the appliances I had bought with his money; the work was going on steadily, successfully, drawing near an end. I was like a man emerging from a thicket, and suddenly coming on some unmeaning tragedy. I went to bury him. My mind was still on this research, and I did not lift a finger to save his character. I remember the funeral, the cheap hearse, the scant ceremony, the windy frost-bitten hillside, and the

16 **lodging-house:** Pension.
20 **thicket:** Dickicht.
21 **unmeaning:** sinn-, bedeutungslos.
23 **hearse:** Leichenwagen.
24 **scant:** karg, schmucklos.
   frost-bitten: frostgeschädigt, erfroren.

old college friend of his who read the service over him, –
a shabby, black, bent old man with a snivelling cold.

I remember walking back to the empty home, through
the place that had once been a village and was now
5 patched and tinkered by the jerry builders into the ugly
likeness of a town. Every way the roads ran out at last
into the desecrated fields and ended in rubble heaps and
rank wet weeds. I remember myself as a gaunt black figure, going along the slippery, shiny pavement, and the
10 strange sense of detachment I felt from the squalid re-
spectability, the sordid commercialism of the place.

I did not feel a bit sorry for my father. He seemed to me
to be the victim of his own foolish sentimentality. The
current cant required my attendance at his funeral, but
15 it was really not my affair.

But going along the High Street, my old life came back
to me for a space, for I met the girl I had known ten years
since. Our eyes met.

Something moved me to turn back and talk to her. She
20 was a very ordinary person.

It was all like a dream, that visit to the old places. I did
not feel then that I was lonely, that I had come out from
the world into a desolate place. I appreciated my loss of

---

2 **to snivel:** schniefen, eine laufende Nase haben.
5 **to tinker:** (zu etwas zusammen)basteln, verpfuschen.
  jerry builder: Erbauer minderwertiger Häuser, Bauschwindler.
7 **to desecrate s.th.:** etwas entweihen.
  rubble: Geröll, Schutt.
8 **rank:** üppig, wuchernd.
  gaunt: hager.
10 **detachment:** Losgelöstsein.
  squalid: schmutzig, abstoßend; schäbig, armselig.
11 **sordid:** schmutzig, gemein, verkommen.
14 **cant:** Heuchelei.

sympathy, but I put it down to the general inanity of
things. Re-entering my room seemed like the recovery
of reality. There were the things I knew and loved. There
stood the apparatus, the experiments arranged and waiting. And now there was scarcely a difficulty left, beyond
the planning of details.

I will tell you, Kemp, sooner or later, all the complicated
processes. We need not go into that now. For the most
part, saving certain gaps I chose to remember, they are
written in cypher in those books that Tramp has hidden.
We must hunt him down. We must get those books
again. But the essential phase was to place the transparent object whose refractive index was to be lowered
between two radiating centres of a sort of ethereal vibration, of which I will tell you more fully later. No, not
these Röntgen vibrations – I don't know that these
others of mine have been described. Yet they are
obvious enough. I needed two little dynamos, and these
I worked with a cheap gas engine. My first experiment
was with a bit of white wool fabric. It was the strangest
thing in the world to see it in the flicker of the flashes
soft and white, and then to watch it fade like a wreath of
smoke and vanish.

I could scarcely believe I had done it. I put my hand into
the emptiness, and there was the thing as solid as ever. I

---

1 **to put s.th. down to s.th. else:** etwas einer anderen Sache zuschreiben.
  inanity: Nichtigkeit, Leere.
11 **to hunt s.o. down:** 1. jdn. aufstöbern; 2. jdn. zur Strecke bringen.
14 **to radiate:** Strahlen aussenden.
14f. **ethereal vibration:** Ätherschwingung.
18 **dynamo:** Maschine zur Erzeugung elektrischen Stroms.
20 **wool fabric:** Wollstoff.
22 **wreath:** Kringel.

felt it awkwardly, and threw it on the floor. I had a little trouble finding it again.

And then came a curious experience. I heard a miaow behind me, and turning, saw a lean white cat, very dirty, on the cistern cover outside the window. A thought came into my head. 'Everything ready for you,' I said, and went to the window, opened it, and called softly. She came in, purring, – the poor beast was starving, – and I gave her some milk. All my food was in a cupboard in the corner of the room. After that she went smelling round the room, – evidently with the idea of making herself at home. The invisible rag upset her a bit; you should have seen her spit at it! But I made her comfortable on the pillow of my truckle-bed. And I gave her butter to get her to wash."

"And you processed her?"

"I processed her. But giving drugs to a cat is no joke, Kemp! And the process failed."

"Failed!"

"In two particulars. These were the claws and the pigment stuff – what is it? – at the back of the eye in a cat. You know?"

"*Tapetum.*"

"Yes, the *tapetum*. It didn't go. After I'd given the stuff

---

4 **lean:** mager.
5 **cistern cover:** Regenwassertonnendeckel.
8 **to purr:** schnurren.
13 **to spit:** fauchen.
14 **truckle-bed:** niedriges Rollbett.
16 **to process s.o.:** jdn. einem Experiment unterziehen.
20 **particular:** einzelner Punkt.
23 **tapetum:** *Tapetum lucidum* (Lat.): lichtreflektierende Netzhautschicht, die das Augenleuchten bei Katzen bewirkt.

to bleach the blood and done certain other things to her,
I gave the beast opium, and put her and the pillow she
was sleeping on, on the apparatus. And after all the rest
had faded and vanished, there remained two little ghosts
of her eyes."

"Odd!"

"I can't explain it. She was bandaged and clamped, of
course, – so I had her safe; but she woke while she was
still misty, and miaowled dismally, and someone came
knocking. It was an old woman from downstairs, who
suspected me of vivisecting, – a drink-sodden old creature, with only a white cat to care for in all the world. I
whipped out some chloroform, and applied it, and answered the door. 'Did I hear a cat?' she asked. 'My cat?'
'Not here,' said I, very politely. She was a little doubtful
and tried to peer past me into the room; strange enough
to her no doubt, – bare walls, uncurtained windows,
truckle-bed, with the gas engine vibrating, and the
seethe of the radiant points, and that faint ghastly stinging of chloroform in the air. She had to be satisfied at last
and went away again."

"How long did it take?" asked Kemp.

1 **to bleach:** bleichen.
7 **to clamp s.th.:** etwas festmachen, -binden.
9 **misty:** 1. unklar, verschwommen (Konturen); 2. benommen.
   to miaowl: Variante zu *to miaow*.
11 **to vivisect:** vivisezieren, eine Vivisektion (operativen Eingriff am le-
   benden Tier) vornehmen.
   drink-sodden: der Trunksucht ergeben.
13 **to whip s.th. out:** etwas schnell hervorholen, (plötzlich) zücken.
19 **seethe:** hier: zischendes Geräusch.
   radiant point: Strahlungspol.
19f. **stinging:** stechender Geruch.

"Three or four hours – the cat. The bones and sinews
and the fat were the last to go, and the tips of the
coloured hairs. And, as I say, the back part of the eye,
tough iridescent stuff it is, wouldn't go at all.

5   It was night outside long before the business was over,
and nothing was to be seen but the dim eyes and the
claws. I stopped the gas engine, felt for and stroked the
beast, which was still insensible, and then, being tired,
left it sleeping on the invisible pillow and went to bed. I

10 found it hard to sleep. I lay awake thinking weak aimless
stuff, going over the experiment over and over again, or
dreaming feverishly of things growing misty and vanishing about me, until everything, the ground I stood on,
vanished, and so I came to that that sickly falling nightmare

15 one gets. About two, the cat began miaowling about the
room. I tried to hush it by talking to it, and then I decided to turn it out. I remember the shock I had when
striking a light – there were just the round eyes shining
green – and nothing round them. I would have given it

20 milk, but I hadn't any. It wouldn't be quiet, it just sat
down and miaowled at the door. I tried to catch it, with
an idea of putting it out of the window, but it wouldn't be
caught, it vanished. Then it began miaowing in different
parts of the room. At last I opened the window and

25 made a bustle. I suppose it went out at last. I never saw
any more of it.
  Then – Heaven knows why – I fell thinking of my father's
funeral again, and the dismal windy hillside, until the

---

1 **sinew:** Sehne.
4 **iridescent:** irisierend.
14 **sickly:** krankhaft; widerlich, widerwärtig.
   nightmare: Alptraum.
25 **to make a bustle:** Rabatz machen.

day had come. I found sleeping was hopeless, and, locking my door after me, wandered out into the morning streets."

"You don't mean to say there's an invisible cat at large!" said Kemp.

"If it hasn't been killed," said the Invisible Man. "Why not?"

"Why not?" said Kemp. "I didn't mean to interrupt."

"It's very probably been killed," said the Invisible Man. "It was alive four days after, I know, and down a grating in Great Tichfield Street; because I saw a crowd round the place, trying to see whence the miaowing came."

He was silent for the best part of a minute. Then he resumed abruptly: –

"I remember that morning before the change very vividly. I must have gone up Great Portland Street. I remember the barracks in Albany Street, and the horse soldiers coming out, and at last I found myself sitting in the sunshine and feeling very ill and strange, on the summit of Primrose Hill. It was a sunny day in January, – one of those sunny, frosty days that came before the snow this year. My weary brain tried to formulate the position, to plot out a plan of action.

I was surprised to find, now that my prize was within my grasp, how inconclusive its attainment seemed. As a matter of fact I was worked out; the intense stress of nearly four years' continuous work left me incapable of

---

10f. **grating:** Gitter (über dem Abfluß).
18 **barracks** (pl.): Kaserne.
24 **to plot out a plan:** einen Plan fassen, schmieden.
26 **inconclusive:** unbestimmt, nicht überzeugend.
　　attainment: Erreichen.

any strength of feeling. I was apathetic, and I tried in
vain to recover the enthusiasm of my first inquiries, the
passion of discovery that had enabled me to compass
even the downfall of my father's grey hairs. Nothing
5 seemed to matter. I saw pretty clearly this was a transient mood, due to overwork and want of sleep, and that
either by drugs or rest it would be possible to recover my
energies.

All I could think clearly was that the thing had to be car-
10 ried through; the fixed idea still ruled me. And soon, for
the money I had was almost exhausted. I looked about
me at the hillside, with children playing and girls watching them, and tried to think of all the fantastic advantages an invisible man would have in the world. After a
15 time I crawled home, took some food and a strong dose
of strychnine, and went to sleep in my clothes on my un-
made bed. Strychnine is a grand tonic, Kemp, to take the
flabbiness out of a man."

"It's the devil," said Kemp. "It's the palaeolithic in a
20 bottle."

"I awoke vastly invigorated and rather irritable. You
know?"

"I know the stuff."

"And there was someone rapping at the door. It was my

---

1 **apathetic:** apathisch, gleichgültig.
3 **to compass:** 1. herbeiführen, bewirken; 2. begreifen.
5f. **transient:** vorübergehend.
16 **strychnine:** giftiges Alkaloid, das in kleineren Dosen stimulierend auf
   Nervensystem, Kreislauf, Muskeln und Atmung wirkt. Regelmäßige
   Einnahme kann zu Suchterscheinungen führen.
17 **tonic:** Stärkungsmittel.
18 **flabbiness:** Schlaffheit.
19 **palaeolithic:** Altsteinzeit.
21 **invigorated:** gestärkt.

landlord with threats and inquiries, an old Polish Jew in
a long grey coat and greasy slippers. I had been torment-
ing a cat in the night, he was sure, – the old woman's
tongue had been busy. He insisted on knowing all about
it. The laws of this country against vivisection were very
severe, – he might be liable. I denied the cat. Then the
vibration of the little gas engine could be felt all over the
house, he said. That was true, certainly. He edged round
me into the room, peering about over his German-silver
spectacles, and a sudden dread came into my mind that
he might carry away something of my secret. I tried to
keep between him and the concentrating apparatus I
had arranged, and that only made him more curious.
What was I doing? Why was I always alone and secretive? Was it legal? Was it dangerous? I paid nothing but
the usual rent. His had always been a most respectable
house – in a disreputable neighbourhood. Suddenly my
temper gave way. I told him to get out. He began to
protest, to jabber of his right of entry. In a moment I had
him by the collar; something ripped, and he went spinning out into his own passage. I slammed and locked the
door and sat down quivering.

1 **landlord:** Hauswirt, Hausherr.
2 **greasy:** speckig, schmutzig.
2f. **to torment:** quälen.
6 **to be liable:** (für etwas) haftbar sein, haften.
9 **German-silver:** Neusilber (Legierung aus Kupfer, Nickel und Zink).
14f. **secretive:** geheimnistuerisch.
17 **disreputable:** verrufen.
17f. **my temper gave way:** mir riß der Geduldsfaden.
19 **to jabber:** plappern, brabbeln.
20 **to rip:** reißen.
22 **to quiver:** zittern, beben.

He made a fuss outside, which I disregarded, and after a
time he went away.

But this brought matters to a crisis. I did not know what
he would do, nor even what he had power to do. To
5 move to fresh apartments would have meant delay; all
together I had barely twenty pounds left in the world, –
for the most part in a bank, – and I could not afford that.
Vanish! It was irresistible. Then there would be an inquiry, the sacking of my room —

10 At the thought of the possibility of my work being exposed or interrupted at its very climax, I became angry
and active. I hurried out with my three books of notes,
my cheque-book, – the tramp has them now, – and directed them from the nearest Post Office to a house of
15 call for letters and parcels in Great Portland Street. I
tried to go out noiselessly. Coming in, I found my landlord going quietly upstairs; he had heard the door close,
I suppose. You would have laughed to see him jump
aside on the landing as I came tearing after him. He
20 glared at me as I went by him, and I made the house
quiver with the slamming of my door. I heard him come
shuffling up to my floor, hesitate, and go down. I set to
work upon my preparations forthwith.

It was all done that evening and night. While I was still
25 sitting under the sickly, drowsy influence of the drugs
that decolourise blood, there came a repeated knocking

1 **to make a fuss:** Krach schlagen, Lärm machen.
9 **sacking:** Durchsuchen, -suchung.
14f. **house of call for letters:** Stelle, an der Briefe zum Abholen depo-
niert sind.
22 **to shuffle:** schlurfen.
25 **drowsy:** einschläfernd.
26 **to decolourise:** entfärben.

at the door. It ceased, footsteps went away and returned, and the knocking was resumed. There was an attempt to push something under the door – a blue paper. Then in a fit of irritation I rose and went and flung the door wide open. 'Now then?' said I.

It was my landlord, with a notice of ejectment or something. He held it out to me, saw something odd about my hands, I expect, and lifted his eyes to my face.

For a moment he gaped. Then he gave a sort of inarticulate cry, dropped candle and writ together, and went blundering down the dark passage to the stairs. I shut the door, locked it, and went to the looking-glass. Then I understood his terror. My face was white – like white stone.

But it was all horrible. I had not expected the suffering. A night of racking anguish, sickness and fainting. I set my teeth, though my skin was presently afire, all my body afire; but I lay there like grim death. I understood now how it was the cat had howled until I chloroformed it. Lucky it was I lived alone and untended in my room. There were times when I sobbed and groaned and talked. But I stuck to it. I became insensible and woke languid in the darkness.

6 **ejectment:** Hinauswerfen; hier: Kündigung.
9f. **inarticulate:** unartikuliert, undeutlich.
10 **writ:** Schriftstück, Verfügung.
16 **racking:** quälend.
   anguish: Pein, Schmerz.
16f. **to set one's teeth:** die Zähne zusammenbeißen.
17 **to be afire:** flammend heiß sein, brennen.
18 **like grim death** (*infml.*): verbissen, verzweifelt (*grim:* grimmig, schrecklich).
20 **untended:** von niemandem versorgt.
23 **languid:** müde, matt.

The pain had passed. I thought I was killing myself and
I did not care. I shall never forget that dawn, and the
strange horror of seeing that my hands had become as
clouded glass, and watching them grow clearer and thin-
5 ner as the day went by, until at last I could see the sickly
disorder of my room through them, though I closed my
transparent eyelids. My limbs became glassy, the bones
and arteries faded, vanished, and the little white nerves
went last. I ground my teeth and stayed there to the end.
10 At last only the dead tips of the finger-nails remained,
pallid and white, and the brown stain of some acid upon
my fingers.

I struggled up. At first I was as incapable as a swathed infant, – stepping with limbs I could not see. I was weak
15 and very hungry. I went and stared at nothing in my
shaving-glass, at nothing save where an attenuated pigment still remained behind the retina of my eyes, fainter
than mist. I had to hang on to the table and press my
forehead to the glass.

20 It was only by a frantic effort of will that I dragged myself back to the apparatus and completed the process.

I slept during the forenoon, pulling the sheet over my
eyes to shut out the light, and about midday I was awak-
ened again by a knocking. My strength had returned.
25 I sat up and listened and heard a whispering. I sprang to

---

4 **clouded glass:** 1. Milch-, Mattglas; 2. blind gewordenes Glas.
9 **to grind one's teeth:** mit den Zähnen knirschen.
11 **pallid:** matt, blaß.
  acid: Säure.
13f. **swathed infant:** Wickelkind.
16 **attenuated:** abgeschwächt, verblaßt.
17 **retina:** Netzhaut.
22 **forenoon** (fml.): Vormittag.

my feet and as noiselessly as possible began to detach
the connections of my apparatus, and to distribute it
about the room, so as to destroy the suggestions of its arrangement. Presently the knocking was renewed and
voices called, first my landlord's, and then two others. To
gain time I answered them. The invisible rag and pillow
came to hand and I opened the window and pitched
them out on to the cistern cover. As the window opened,
a heavy crash came at the door. Someone had charged it
with the idea of smashing the lock. But the stout bolts I
had screwed up some days before stopped him. That
startled me, made me angry. I began to tremble and do
things hurriedly.

I tossed together some loose paper, straw, packing paper
and so forth, in the middle of the room, and turned on
the gas. Heavy blows began to rain upon the door. I
could not find the matches. I beat my hands on the wall
with rage. I turned down the gas again, stepped out of
the window on the cistern cover, very softly lowered the
sash, and sat down, secure and invisible, but quivering
with anger, to watch events. They split a panel, I saw, and
in another moment they had broken away the staples of
the bolts and stood in the open doorway. It was the landlord and his two step-sons, sturdy young men of three or
four and twenty. Behind them fluttered the old hag of a
woman from downstairs.

1 **to detach:** lösen, entfernen, abtrennen.
3 **suggestion:** (fig.) Spur, Hinweis.
7 **to pitch:** werfen, schleudern.
22 **staple:** Schließklappe.
24 **step-son:** Stiefsohn.
   sturdy: kräftig (gebaut).
25 **hag:** Hexe, häßliches altes Weib.

You may imagine their astonishment on finding the
room empty. One of the younger men rushed to the window at once, flung it up and stared out. His staring eyes
and thick-lipped bearded face came a foot from my face.
5 I was half minded to hit his silly countenance, but I arrested my doubled fist. He stared right through me. So
did the others as they joined him. The old man went and
peered under the bed, and then they all made a rush for
the cupboard. They had to argue about it at length in
10 Yiddish and Cockney English. They concluded I had not
answered them, that their imagination had deceived
them. A feeling of extraordinary elation took the place
of my anger as I sat outside the window and watched
these four people – for the old lady came in, glancing
15 suspiciously about her like a cat, trying to understand
the riddle of my behaviour.

The old man, so far as I could understand his *patois*,
agreed with the old lady that I was a vivisectionist. The
sons protested in garbled English that I was an electri-
20 cian, and appealed to the dynamos and radiators. They
were all nervous against my arrival, although I found
subsequently that they had bolted the front door. The
old lady peered into the cupboard and under the bed,

---

5 **countenance** (arch.): Gesicht.
6 **to double:** (Faust) ballen.
10 **Yiddish:** Jiddisch (aus mittelhochdeutschen, hebräischen und slawi-
schen Elementen gemischte Sprache der osteuropäischen Juden).
12 **elation:** freudige Erregung.
17 **patois** (Fr.): Dialekt; hier: Kauderwelsch.
19 **garbled:** verstümmelt.
20 **to appeal to s.th.:** auf etwas verweisen.
radiator: 1. Heizgerät; 2. Kühler.
21 **to be nervous against s.th.:** Angst vor etwas haben.

and one of the young men pushed up the register and
stared up the chimney. One of my fellow lodgers, a
costermonger who shared the opposite room with a
butcher, appeared on the landing, and he was called in
and told incoherent things.

It occurred to me that the radiators, if they fell into the
hands of some acute well-educated person, would give
me away too much, and watching my opportunity, I
came into the room and tilted one of the little dynamos
off its fellow on which it was standing, and smashed both
apparatus. Then, while they were trying to explain the
smash, I dodged out of the room and went softly downstairs.

I went into one of the sitting-rooms and waited until
they came down, still speculating and argumentative, all
a little disappointed at finding no 'horrors,' and all a little puzzled how they stood with regard to me. Then I
slipped up again with a box of matches, fired my heap of
paper and rubbish, put the chairs and bedding thereby,
led the gas to the affair, by means of an india-rubber
tube, and waving a farewell to the room left it for the last
time."

"You fired the house!" exclaimed Kemp.

"Fired the house. It was the only way to cover my trail –
and no doubt it was insured. I slipped the bolts of the
front door quietly and went out into the street. I was in-

---

1 **register:** Klappe, Schieber.
3 **costermonger** (BE): Obsthändler.
7 **acute:** scharfsinnig.
7f. **to give s.o. away:** jdn. verraten, entlarven.
9f. **to tilt s.th. off s.th. else:** etwas von etwas anderem herunterkippen.
12 **to dodge:** schlüpfen.
20 f. **india-rubber tube:** Gummischlauch.

visible, and I was only just beginning to realise the extraordinary advantage my invisibility gave me. My head
was already teeming with plans of all the wild and won-
4 derful things I had now impunity to do."

Chapter XXI

In Oxford Street

"In going downstairs the first time I found an unex-
pected difficulty because I could not see my feet; indeed
I stumbled twice, and there was an unaccustomed clum-
10 siness in gripping the bolt. By not looking down, however, I managed to walk on the level passably well.
My mood, I say, was one of exaltation. I felt as a seeing
man might do, with padded feet and noiseless clothes, in
a city of the blind. I experienced a wild impulse to jest,
15 to startle people, to clap men on the back, fling people's
hats astray, and generally revel in my extraordinary advantage.

3 **to teem with s.th.:** von etwas wimmeln, vor etwas strotzen.
4 **to have impunity to do s.th.:** ungestraft, gefahrlos etwas tun (kön-
    nen).
9 **unaccustomed:** ungewohnt.
9f. **clumsiness:** Unbeholfenheit.
12 **exaltation:** Begeisterung, Erregung.
13 **padded:** gepolstert.
14 **to jest:** Schabernack treiben.
15f. **to fling s.o.'s hat astray:** jdm. den Hut vom Kopf schlagen (*astray*
    [adv.]: in die Irre).
16 **to revel:** schwelgen.

But hardly had I emerged upon Great Portland Street,
however (my lodging was close to the big draper's shop
there), when I heard a clashing concussion and was hit
violently behind, and turning saw a man carrying a basket of soda-water syphons, and looking in amazement at
his burden. Although the blow had really hurt me, I
found something so irresistible in his astonishment that
I laughed aloud. 'The devil's in the basket,' I said, and
suddenly twisted it out of his hand. He let go incontinently, and I swung the whole weight into the air.
But a fool of a cabman, standing outside a public house,
made a sudden rush for this, and his extending fingers
took me with excruciating violence under the ear. I let
the whole down with a smash on the cabman, and then,
with shouts and the clatter of feet about me, people coming out of shops, vehicles pulling up, I realised what I
had done for myself, and cursing my folly, backed
against a shop window and prepared to dodge out of the
confusion. In a moment I should be wedged into a crowd
and inevitably discovered. I pushed by a butcher boy,
who luckily did not turn to see the nothingness that
shoved him aside, and dodged behind the cabman's four-
wheeler. I do not know how they settled the business. I
hurried straight across the road, which was happily clear,
and hardly heeding which way I went, in the fright of detection the incident had given me, plunged into the
afternoon throng of Oxford Street.

1 **to emerge upon s.th.:** auf etwas hinaustreten.
2 **draper:** Tuch-, Textilhändler.
3 **clashing:** klirrend, rasselnd.
13 **excruciating:** heftig, entsetzlich.
19 **to be wedged:** eingekeilt sein.
25f. **detection:** Entdeckung.
27 **throng:** Gedränge.

I tried to get into the stream of people, but they were too
thick for me, and in a moment my heels were being trod-
den upon. I took to the gutter, the roughness of which I
found painful to my feet, and forthwith the shaft of a
crawling hansom dug me forcibly under the shoulder
blade, reminding me that I was already bruised severely.
I staggered out of the way of the cab, avoided a perambulator by a convulsive movement, and found myself behind the hansom. A happy thought saved me, and as this
drove slowly along I followed in its immediate wake,
trembling and astonished at the turn of my adventure.
And not only trembling, but shivering. It was a bright
day in January and I was stark naked and the thin slime
of mud that covered the road was freezing. Foolish as it
seems to me now, I had not reckoned that, transparent
or not, I was still amenable to the weather and all its consequences.

Then suddenly a bright idea came into my head. I ran
round and got into the cab. And so, shivering, scared,
and sniffing with the first intimations of a cold, and with
the bruises in the small of my back growing upon my attention, I drove slowly along Oxford Street and past Tottenham Court Road. My mood was as different from
that in which I had sallied forth ten minutes ago as it is

---

3 **gutter:** Rinnstein.
4 **shaft:** Deichsel.
5 **hansom:** zweirädrige Droschke mit Verdeck.
  forcibly (adv.): heftig, mit Gewalt.
7f. **perambulator** (fml.): Kinderwagen.
10 **to follow in the wake of s.th.:** (fig.) im Kielwasser von etwas segeln,
  etwas auf dem Fuß folgen.
16 **to be amenable to s.th.:** einer Sache ausgesetzt, unterworfen sein.
20 **intimation:** Andeutung, Anzeichen.
24 **to sally forth** (auch: *to sally out*) (arch.): sich aufmachen, aufbrechen.

possible to imagine. *This* invisibility indeed! The one thought that possessed me was – how was I to get out of the scrape I was in.

We crawled past Mudie's, and there a tall woman with five or six yellow-labelled books hailed my cab, and I sprang out just in time to escape her, shaving a railway van narrowly in my flight. I made off up the roadway to Bloomsbury Square, intending to strike north past the Museum and so get into the quiet district. I was now cruelly chilled, and the strangeness of my situation so unnerved me that I whimpered as I ran. At the northward corner of the Square a little white dog ran out of the Pharmaceutical Society's offices, and incontinently made for me, nose down.

I had never realised it before, but the nose is to the mind of a dog what the eye is to the mind of a seeing man. Dogs perceive the scent of a man moving as men perceive his vision. This brute began barking and leaping, showing, as it seemed to me, only too plainly that he was aware of me. I crossed Great Russell Street, glancing over my shoulder as I did so, and went some way along Montagu Street before I realised what I was running towards.

Then I became aware of a blare of music, and looking along the street saw a number of people advancing out of Russell Square, red shirts, and the banner of the Sal-

---

4 **Mudie's:** bekannte Leihbücherei in der New Oxford Street.
5 **to hail a cab:** eine Kutsche, Droschke rufen.
6 **to shave:** streifen.
9 **Museum:** *British Museum*.
11 **to whimper:** wimmern.
24 **blare:** Schmettern, Schallen.
26f. **Salvation Army:** Heilsarmee.

vation Army to the fore. Such a crowd, chanting in the
roadway and scoffing on the pavement, I could not hope
to penetrate, and dreading to go back and farther from
home again, and deciding on the spur of the moment, I
5 ran up the white steps of a house facing the museum rail-
ings, and stood there until the crowd should have passed.
Happily the dog stopped at the noise of the band too,
hesitated, and turned tail, running back to Bloomsbury
Square again.
10 On came the band, bawling with unconscious irony some
hymn about 'When shall we see his Face?' and it seemed
an interminable time to me before the tide of the crowd
washed along the pavement by me. Thud, thud, thud,
came the drum with a vibrating resonance, and for the
15 moment I did not notice two urchins stopping at the rail-
ings by me. 'See 'em,' said one. 'See what?' said the
other. 'Why – them footmarks – *bare*. Like what you
makes in mud.'
I looked down and saw the youngsters had stopped and
20 were gaping at the muddy footmarks I had left behind
me up the newly whitened steps. The passing people el-
bowed and jostled them, but their confounded intelligence was arrested. 'Thud, thud, thud, When, thud, shall

---

1 **to the fore:** an der Spitze.
   to chant: 1. singen; 2. Sprechchöre anstimmen.
2 **to scoff:** spotten, höhnen.
4 **on the spur of the moment:** ganz spontan.
5f. **railing:** Geländer.
8 **to turn tail:** die Flucht ergreifen.
12 **tide:** (fig.) Flut, Strom.
15 **urchin:** Gassenjunge, Range.
16 **see 'em?** (dial.): *do you see them?*
22 **to jostle s.o.:** jdn. an-, wegstoßen.
23 **to arrest** (fig.): erregen, fesseln.

we see, thud, his face, thud, thud.' 'There's a barefoot man gone up them steps, or I don't know nothing,' said one. 'And he ain't never come down again. And his foot was a-bleeding.'

5 The thick of the crowd had already passed. 'Looky there, Ted,' quoth the younger of the detectives, with the sharpness of surprise in his voice, and pointed straight to my feet. I looked down and saw at once the dim suggestion of their outline sketched in splashes of mud. For a
10 moment I was paralysed.

'Why, that's rum,' said the elder. 'Dashed rum! It's just like the ghost of a foot, ain't it?' He hesitated and advanced with outstretched hand. A man pulled up short to see what he was catching, and then a girl. In another
15 moment he would have touched me. Then I saw what to do. I made a step, the boy started back with an exclamation, and with a rapid movement I swung myself over into the portico of the next house. But the smaller boy was sharp-eyed enough to follow the movement, and be-
20 fore I was well down the steps and upon the pavement, he had recovered from his momentary astonishment and was shouting out that the feet had gone over the wall. They rushed round and saw my new footmarks flash into being on the lower step and upon the pavement. 'What's

---

3 **he ain't never** (dial.): *he hasn't ever*.
5 **thick** (arch.): Getümmel, Gewoge.
  looky (dial.): *look ye: look* (you).
6 **quoth:** Prät. von *to quethe* (arch.): sagen, sprechen.
8f. **suggestion:** Andeutung.
9 **splash of mud:** Schlammpfütze.
10 **paralysed:** (wie) gelähmt, starr.
11 **dashed rum!** (BE, slang, arch.): verflixt komisch!
18 **portico:** Säulenvorbau (am Eingang), -gang.
23f. **to flash into being:** plötzlich sichtbar werden.

up?' asked someone. 'Feet! Look! Feet running!' Everybody in the road, except my three pursuers, was pouring
along after the Salvation Army, and this not only im-
peded me but them. There was an eddy of surprise and
5 interrogation. At the cost of bowling over one young fellow I got through, and in another moment I was rushing
headlong round the circuit of Russell Square, with six or
seven astonished people following my footmarks. There
was no time for explanation, or else the whole host
10 would have been after me.

Twice I doubled round corners, thrice I crossed the road
and came back on my tracks, and then, as my feet grew
hot and dry, the damp impressions began to fade. At last
I had a breathing space and rubbed my feet clean with
15 my hands, and so got away altogether. The last I saw of
the chase was a little group of a dozen people perhaps,
studying with infinite perplexity a slowly drying footprint that had resulted from a puddle in Tavistock
Square, – a footprint as isolated and incomprehensible
20 to them as Crusoe's solitary discovery.

This running warmed me to a certain extent, and I went

2f. **to pour along:** (fig.) dahinströmen, -ziehen.
3f. **to impede:** (be)hindern.
4 **eddy:** (fig.) Wirbel, Durcheinander.
5 **to bowl s.o. over:** jdn. umstoßen, -werfen.
7 **circuit:** Kreis, Runde.
9 **host:** Menge.
11 **to double round a corner:** um eine Ecke biegen.
14 **breathing space:** Atempause.
18 **puddle:** Pfütze.
20 **Crusoe:** Titelheld des Romans *Robinson Crusoe* (1720/21) von Da-
niel Defoe (um 1660–1731).
solitary: einsam.
21 **to a certain extent:** bis zu einem gewissen Grad.

on with a better courage through the maze of less fre-
quented roads that runs hereabouts. My back had now
become very stiff and sore, my tonsils were painful from
the cabman's fingers, and the skin of my neck had been
scratched by his nails; my feet hurt exceedingly and I was
lame from a little cut on one foot. I saw in time a blind
man approaching me, and fled limping, for I feared his
subtle intuitions. Once or twice accidental collisions occurred and I left people amazed, with unaccountable
curses ringing in their ears. Then came something silent
and quiet against my face, and across the Square fell a
thin veil of slowly falling flakes of snow. I had caught a
cold, and do as I would I could not avoid an occasional
sneeze. And every dog that came in sight, with its point-
ing nose and curious sniffing, was a terror to me.

Then came men and boys running, first one and then
others, and shouting as they ran. It was a fire. They ran
in the direction of my lodging, and looking back down a
street I saw a mass of black smoke streaming up above
the roofs and telephone wires. It was my lodging burning; my clothes, my apparatus, all my resources indeed,
except my cheque-book and the three volumes of
memoranda that awaited me in Great Portland Street,
were there. Burning! I had burnt my boats – if ever a
man did! The place was blazing."

The Invisible Man paused and thought. Kemp glanced
nervously out of the window. "Yes?" he said. "Go on."

---

1 **maze:** Labyrinth.
3 **tonsils:** (Rachen-)Mandeln.
7 **to limp:** hinken.
8 **subtle:** feinsinnig, einfühlsam.
9 **unaccountable:** unerklärlich, rätselhaft.
21 **resources** (pl.): Mittel, Habe.
24 **to burn one's boats** (fig.): alle Brücken hinter sich abbrechen.

Chapter XXII

In the Emporium

"So last January, with the beginnings of a snowstorm in
the air about me – and if it settled on me it would betray
5 me! – weary, cold, painful, inexpressibly wretched, and
still but half convinced of my invisible quality, I began
this new life to which I am committed. I had no refuge,
no appliances, no human being in the world in whom I
could confide. To have told my secret would have given
10 me away – made a mere show and rarity of me. Nevertheless, I was half minded to accost some passer-by and
throw myself upon his mercy. But I knew too clearly the
terror and brutal cruelty my advances would evoke. I
made no plans in the street. My sole object was to get
15 shelter from the snow, to get myself covered and warm;
then I might hope to plan. But even to me, an Invisible
Man, the rows of London houses stood latched, barred,
and bolted impregnably.

Only one thing could I see clearly before me, the cold ex-
20 posure and misery of the snowstorm and the night.

And then I had a brilliant idea. I turned down one of the
roads leading from Gower Street to Tottenham Court

---

2 **emporium** (fml.): Waren-, Kaufhaus.
5 **inexpressibly** (adv.): unsäglich.
7 **to be committed to s.th.:** hier: zu etwas verdammt, einer Sache aus-
   geliefert sein.
11 **to accost s.o.:** jdn. ansprechen.
13 **to evoke:** hervorrufen, auslösen.
14 **sole:** einzig, alleinig.
17 **to latch:** zuschnappen (lassen), schließen.
19f. **exposure:** Ausgesetztsein.

Road, and found myself outside Omniums, the big es-
tablishment where everything is to be bought, – you
know the place, – meat, grocery, linen, furniture, clothing, oil paintings even, – a huge meandering collection of
shops rather than a shop. I had thought I should find the
doors open, but they were closed, and as I stood in the
wide entrance a carriage stopped outside, and a man
in uniform – you know the kind of personage with
'*Omnium*' on his cap – flung open the door. I contrived
to enter, and walking down the shop – it was a department where they were selling ribbons and gloves and
stockings and that kind of thing – came to a more spacious region devoted to picnic baskets and wicker furniture.
I did not feel safe there, however; people were going to
and fro, and I prowled restlessly about until I came upon
a huge section in an upper floor containing scores and
hundreds of bedsteads, and beyond these I found a rest-
ing-place at last among a huge pile of folded flock mattresses. The place was already lit up and agreeably
warm, and I decided to remain where I was, keeping a
cautious eye on the two or three sets of shopmen and
customers who were meandering through the place until
closing time came. Then I should be able, I thought,
to rob the place for food and clothing, and disguised,
prowl through it and examine its resources, perhaps

---

1 **Omniums:** sprechender Name (von lat. *omnis* ›ganz, gesamt‹;
  ›alle[r, -s]‹).
4 **meandering:** sich dahinschlängelnd.
9f. **to contrive to do s.th.:** es fertigbringen, etwas zu tun.
13 **wicker:** Korb-.
18 **bedstead:** Bettstelle, Bett.
19f. **flock matress:** Wollmatraze.

sleep on some of the bedding. That seemed an acceptable plan. My idea was to procure clothing to make myself a muffled but acceptable figure, to get money, and
then to recover my books and parcels where they
5 awaited me, take a lodging somewhere and elaborate
plans for the complete realisation of the advantages my
invisibility gave me (as I still imagined) over my fellow-
men.

Closing time arrived quickly enough; it could not have
10 been more than an hour after I took up my position on
the mattresses before I noticed the blinds of the windows being drawn, and customers being marched door-
ward. And then a number of brisk young men began
with remarkable alacrity to tidy up the goods that re-
15 mained disturbed. I left my lair as the crowds diminished, and prowled cautiously out into the less desolate
parts of the shop. I was really surprised to observe how
rapidly the young men and women whipped away the
goods displayed for sale during the day. All the boxes of
20 goods, the hanging fabrics, the festoons of lace, the
boxes of sweets in the grocery section, the displays of
this and that, were being whipped down, folded up,
slapped into tidy receptacles, and everything that could
not be taken down and put away had sheets of some
25 coarse stuff like sacking flung over it. Finally all the
chairs were turned up on to the counters, leaving the

---

15 **lair:** Lager; Schlupfwinkel, Versteck.
20 **festoon:** Girlande.
   lace: Spitze (Stoff).
23 **to slap:** stecken, schnell verstauen.
   receptacle: Behälter.
25 **sacking:** Sackleinen.

169 In the Emporium

floor clear. Directly each of these young people had done, he or she made promptly for the door with such an expression of animation as I have rarely observed in a shop assistant before. Then came a lot of youngsters scattering sawdust and carrying pails and brooms. I had to dodge to get out of the way, and as it was, my ankle got stung with the sawdust. For some time, wandering through the swathed and darkened departments, I could hear the brooms at work. And at last a good hour or more after the shop had been closed, came a noise of locking doors. Silence came upon the place, and I found myself wandering through the vast and intricate shops, galleries and showrooms of the place, alone. It was very still; in one place I remember passing near one of the Tottenham Court Road entrances and listening to the tapping of boot-heels of the passers-by.

My first visit was to the place where I had seen stockings and gloves for sale. It was dark, and I had the devil of a hunt after matches, which I found at last in the drawer of the little cash desk. Then I had to get a candle. I had to tear down wrappings and ransack a number of boxes and drawers, but at last I managed to turn out what I sought; the box label called them lambswool pants, and lambs-wool vests. Then socks, a thick comforter, and then I went to the clothing place and got trousers, a lounge

---

1 f. **Directly each of these young people had done:** Unmittelbar nach-
    dem jeder der jungen Leute seine Arbeit erledigt hatte.
4 **shop assistant:** Verkäufer(in).
5 **sawdust:** Sägemehl.
12 **intricate:** verwinkelt, verwirrend angelegt.
18 f. **I had the devil of a hunt** (infml.): ich mußte verflucht lange suchen.
23 **pants:** Unterhose(n).
24 **comforter:** langer wollener Schal (BE).
25 f. **lounge jacket:** Sakko.

jacket, an overcoat and a slouch hat, – a clerical sort of
hat with the brim turned down. I began to feel a human
being again, and my next thought was food.

Upstairs was a refreshment department, and there I got
5 cold meat. There was coffee still in the urn, and I lit the
gas and warmed it up again, and altogether I did not do
badly. Afterwards, prowling through the place in search
of blankets, – I had to put up at last with a heap of down
quilts, – I came upon a grocery section with a lot of
10 chocolate and candied fruits, more than was good for me
indeed – and some white burgundy. And near that was a
toy department, and I had a brilliant idea. I found some
artificial noses – dummy noses, you know, and I thought
of dark spectacles. But Omniums had no optical depart-
15 ment. My nose had been a difficulty indeed – I had
thought of paint. But the discovery set my mind running
on wigs and masks and the like. Finally I went to sleep in
a heap of down quilts, very warm and comfortable.

My last thoughts before sleeping were the most agree-
20 able I had had since the change. I was in a state of
physical serenity, and that was reflected in my mind. I
thought that I should be able to slip out unobserved in
the morning with my clothes upon me, muffling my face
with a white wrapper I had taken, purchase, with the
25 money I had taken, spectacles and so forth, and so com-

---

1 **clerical:** geistlich, Priester-.
5 **urn:** Kaffeemaschine.
8 **to put up with s.th.:** sich mit etwas abfinden, abgeben.
8f. **down quilt:** Daunendecke.
11 **burgundy:** Burgunder(wein).
13 **dummy:** Attrappe.
17 **wig:** Perücke.
21 **serenity:** Ruhe, Zufriedenheit.

plete my disguise. I lapsed into disorderly dreams of all the fantastic things that had happened during the last few days. I saw the ugly little Jew of a landlord vociferating in his rooms; I saw his two sons marvelling, and the wrinkled old woman's gnarled face as she asked for her cat. I experienced again the strange sensation of seeing the cloth disappear, and so I came round to the windy hillside and the sniffing old clergyman mumbling 'Dust to dust, earth to earth,' and my father's open grave.

'You also,' said a voice, and suddenly I was being forced towards the grave. I struggled, shouted, appealed to the mourners, but they continued stonily following the service; the old clergyman, too, never faltered droning and sniffing through the ritual. I realised I was invisible and inaudible, that overwhelming forces had their grip on me. I struggled in vain, I was forced over the brink, the coffin rang hollow as I fell upon it, and the gravel came flying after me in spadefuls. Nobody heeded me, nobody was aware of me. I made convulsive struggles and awoke.

The pale London dawn had come, the place was full of a chilly grey light that filtered round the edges of the win-

---

1 **to lapse into s.th.:** in etwas verfallen.
3 f. **to vociferate:** schreien, brüllen.
5 **wrinkled:** faltig, runzlig.
gnarled: zerfurcht.
8 **to mumble:** murmeln.
12 **mourner:** Trauergast.
stonily (adv.): unerschütterlich.
13 **to falter:** wanken, zögern.
to drone: monoton reden, leiern.
15 **inaudible:** unhörbar.
16 **brink:** Rand.
22 **to filter:** sickern, strömen.

dow-blinds. I sat up, and for a time I could not think
where this ample apartment, with its counters, its piles of
rolled stuff, its heap of quilts and cushions, its iron pil-
lars, might be. Then, as recollection came back to me, I
5 heard voices in conversation.

Then far down the place, in the brighter light of
some department which had already raised its blinds, I
saw two men approaching. I scrambled to my feet,
looking about me for some way of escape, and even as
10 I did so the sound of my movement made them aware
of me. I suppose they saw merely a figure moving
quietly and quickly away. 'Who's that?' cried one, and
'Stop there!' shouted the other. I dashed round a corner and came full tilt – a faceless figure, mind you! – on
15 a lanky lad of fifteen. He yelled and I bowled him over,
rushed past him, turned another corner, and by a happy
inspiration threw myself flat behind a counter. In another moment feet went running past and I heard
voices shouting, 'All hands to the doors!' asking what
20 was 'up', and giving one another advice how to catch
me.

Lying on the ground, I felt scared out of my wits. But –
odd as it may seem – it did not occur to me at the moment to take off my clothes as I should have done. I had
25 made up my mind, I suppose, to get away in them, and

---

2 **ample:** weit, geräumig.
3 f. **pillar:** Pfeiler, Säule.
4 **recollection:** Erinnerung.
8 **to scramble to one's feet:** sich aufrappeln.
14 **full tilt:** mit voller Wucht.
15 **lanky:** hochaufgeschossen.
22 (*to be*) **scared out of one's wits** (infml.): fürchterliche Angst haben.
25 **to make up one's mind to do s.th.:** sich entschließen, etwas zu tun.

that ruled me. And then down the vista of the counters
came a bawling of 'Here he is!'
I sprang to my feet, whipped a chair off the counter, and
sent it whirling at the fool who had shouted, turned,
came into another round a corner, sent him spinning,
and rushed up the stairs. He kept his footing, gave a view
hallo! and came up the staircase hot after me. Up the
staircase were piled a multitude of those bright-coloured
pot things – what are they?"

"Art pots," suggested Kemp.

"That's it! Art pots. Well, I turned at the top step and
swung round, plucked one out of a pile and smashed it
on his silly head as he came at me. The whole pile of pots
went headlong, and I heard shouting and footsteps running from all parts. I made a mad rush for the refreshment place, and there was a man in white like a man
cook, who took up the chase. I made one last desperate
turn and found myself among lamps and ironmongery. I
went behind the counter of this, and waited for my cook,
and as he bolted in at the head of the chase, I doubled
him up with a lamp. Down he went, and I crouched behind the counter and began whipping off my clothes as
fast as I could. Coat, jacket, trousers, shoes were all
right, but a lambswool vest fits a man like a skin. I heard
more men coming, my cook was lying quiet on the other

---

1 **vista:** lange Reihe, Kette.
6 **footing:** fester Halt.
6f. **view hallo!:** Halloruf beim Erscheinen des Fuchses während der
   Fuchsjagd.
7 **hot after me:** mir dicht auf den Fersen.
18 **ironmongery:** Eisenwaren.
20f. **to double s.o. up:** jdn. niederschlagen, zu Fall bringen.
21 **to crouch:** sich ducken, kauern.

side of the counter, stunned or scared speechless, and I
had to make another dash for it, like a rabbit hunted out
of a wood-pile.

'This way, policeman!' I heard someone shouting. I
found myself in my bedstead store-room again, and at
the end a wilderness of wardrobes. I rushed among
them, went flat, got rid of my vest after infinite wriggling, and stood a free man again, panting and scared, as
the policeman and three of the shopmen came round the
corner. They made a rush for the vest and pants, and collared the trousers. 'He's dropping his plunder,' said one
of the young men. 'He *must* be somewhere here.'

But they did not find me all the same.

I stood watching them hunt for me for a time, and cursing my ill-luck in losing the clothes. Then I went into the
refreshment-room, drank a little milk I found there, and
sat down by the fire to consider my position.

In a little while two assistants came in and began to talk
over the business very excitedly and like the fools they
were. I heard a magnified account of my depredations,
and other speculations as to my whereabouts. Then I fell
to scheming again. The insurmountable difficulty of the
place, especially now it was alarmed, was to get any
plunder out of it. I went down into the warehouse to see
if there was any chance of packing and addressing a parcel, but I could not understand the system of checking.
About eleven o'clock, the snow having thawed as it fell,

---

5 **store-room:** Lagerraum.
6 **wilderness:** Wildnis, Wüste, Durcheinander; hier auch: große Menge.
11 **plunder:** Beute, Raub.
20 **magnified:** übertrieben.
  depredation: Verwüstung, Raubzug, Plünderung.
22 **insurmountable:** unüberwindlich.

and the day being finer and a little warmer than the previous one, I decided that the Emporium was hopeless, and went out again, exasperated at my want of success, with only the vaguest plans of action in my mind."

Chapter XXIII

In Drury Lane

"But you begin to realise now," said the Invisible Man, "the full disadvantage of my condition. I had no shelter, no covering. To get clothing was to forego all my advantage, to make of myself a strange and terrible thing. I was fasting; for to eat, to fill myself with unassimilated matter, would be to become grotesquely visible again."

"I never thought of that," said Kemp.

"Nor had I. And the snow had warned me of other dangers. I could not go abroad in snow – it would settle on me and expose me. Rain, too, would make me a watery outline, a glistening surface of a man – a bubble. And fog – I should be like a fainter bubble in a fog, a surface, a greasy glimmer of humanity. Moreover, as I went abroad – in the London air – I gathered dirt about my ankles, floating smuts and dust upon my skin. I did not know

---

3 **to exasperate:** verärgern, zur Verzweiflung bringen.
9 **to forego s.th.:** auf etwas verzichten, etwas aufgeben.
11 **unassimilated:** unverdaut.
17 **to glisten:** glänzen, glitzern.
21 **to float:** schweben, treiben.
   smut: Rußflocke.

how long it would be before I should become visible
from that cause also. But I saw clearly it could not be for
long.
Not in London at any rate.

5 I went into the slums towards Great Portland Street, and
found myself at the end of the street in which I had
lodged. I did not go that way, because of the crowd halfway down it opposite to the still smoking ruins of the
house I had fired. My most immediate problem was to
10 get clothing. What to do with my face puzzled me. Then
I saw in one of those little miscellaneous shops – news,
sweets, toys, stationery, belated Christmas tomfoolery,
and so forth – an array of masks and noses. I realised
that problem was solved. In a flash I saw my course. I
15 turned about, no longer aimless, and went – circuitously
in order to avoid the busy ways, towards the back streets
north of the Strand; for I remembered, though not very
distinctly where, that some theatrical costumiers had
shops in that district.
20 The day was cold, with a nipping wind down the northward running streets. I walked fast to avoid being over-
taken. Every crossing was a danger, every passenger a
thing to watch alertly. One man as I was about to pass
him at the top of Bedford Street, turned upon me
25 abruptly and came into me, sending me into the road
and almost under the wheel of a passing hansom. The

---

11 **miscellaneous shop:** Gemischtwarenladen.
12 **stationery:** Schreibwaren.
   tomfoolery: Blödsinn; hier: Scherzartikel.
13 **array:** Menge.
15 **circuitously** (adv.): umständlich, auf Umwegen.
18 **costumier:** Kostümverleiher.
20 **nipping:** scharf, beißend.

verdict of the cab-rank was that he had had some sort of stroke. I was so unnerved by this encounter that I went into Covent Garden Market and sat down for some time in a quiet corner by a stall of violets, panting and trembling. I found I had caught a fresh cold, and had to turn out after a time lest my sneezes should attract attention.

At last I reached the object of my quest, a dirty fly-blown little shop in a byway near Drury Lane, with a window full of tinsel robes, sham jewels, wigs, slippers, dominoes and theatrical photographs. The shop was old-fashioned and low and dark, and the house rose above it for four storeys, dark and dismal. I peered through the window and, seeing no one within, entered. The opening of the door set a clanking bell ringing. I left it open, and walked round a bare costume stand, into a corner behind a cheval glass. For a minute or so no one came. Then I heard heavy feet striding across a room, and a man appeared down the shop.

My plans were now perfectly definite. I proposed to make my way into the house, secrete myself upstairs,

---

1 **verdict:** Aussage, Urteil.
  cab-rank: Droschkenstand, -halteplatz; hier (fig.): (am Halteplatz wartende) Kutscher.
6 **lest** (fml.): damit nicht, aus Furcht daß.
8 **quest:** Suche.
  fly-blown: von Fliegendreck verschmutzt, schmutzig.
9 **byway:** Seitengasse.
10 **tinsel:** Flitter.
  sham: unecht.
  domino: Domino (langer, als Maskenkostüm getragener Mantel mit Kapuze und weiten Ärmeln).
15 **to clank:** rasseln, klirren, scheppern.
16f. **cheval glass:** hoher Stehspiegel.
21 **to secrete o.s.:** sich unbemerkt schleichen.

watch my opportunity, and when everything was quiet,
rummage out a wig, mask, spectacles, and costume, and
go into the world, perhaps a grotesque but still a credible
figure. And incidentally of course I could rob the house
5 of any available money.

The man who had entered the shop was a short, slight,
hunched, beetle-browed man, with long arms and very
short bandy legs. Apparently I had interrupted a meal.
He stared about the shop with an expression of expecta-
10 tion. This gave way to surprise, and then anger, as he saw
the shop empty. 'Damn the boys!' he said. He went to
stare up and down the street. He came in again in a minute, kicked the door to with his foot spitefully, and went
muttering back to the house door.

15 I came forward to follow him, and at the noise of my
movement he stopped dead. I did so too, startled by his
quickness of ear. He slammed the house door in my
face.

I stood hesitating. Suddenly I heard his quick footsteps
20 returning, and the door reopened. He stood looking
about the shop like one who was still not satisfied. Then,
murmuring to himself, he examined the back of the
counter and peered behind some fixtures. Then he stood
doubtful. He had left the house door open and I slipped
25 into the inner room.

---

2 **to rummage s.th. out:** etwas hervorkramen.
4 **incidentally** (adv.): nebenbei.
6 **slight:** schmächtig.
7 **hunched:** buckelig.
   beetle-browed: mit buschigen Augenbrauen.
8 **bandy legs:** O-Beine.
13 **spitefully** (adv.): böse, zornig.
16 **to stop dead:** plötzlich innehalten.
23 **fixture:** Inventar, Zubehör, Einrichtungsgegenstände.

It was a queer little room, poorly furnished and with a
number of big masks in the corner. On the table was his
belated breakfast, and it was a confoundedly exasperating thing for me, Kemp, to have to sniff his coffee and
stand watching while he came in and resumed his meal.
And his table manners were irritating. Three doors
opened into the little room, one going upstairs and one
down, but they were all shut. I could not get out of the
room while he was there, I could scarcely move because
of his alertness, and there was a draught down my back.
Twice I strangled a sneeze just in time.

The spectacular quality of my sensations was curious
and novel, but for all that I was heartily tired and angry
long before he had done his eating. But at last he made
an end and putting his beggarly crockery on the black tin
tray upon which he had had his teapot, and gathering all
the crumbs up on the mustard-stained cloth, he took the
whole lot of things after him. His burden prevented his
shutting the door behind him, – as he would have done;
I never saw such a man for shutting doors, – and I followed him into a very dirty underground kitchen and
scullery. I had the pleasure of seeing him begin to wash
up, and then, finding no good in keeping down there,
and the brick floor being cold to my feet, I returned upstairs and sat in his chair by the fire. It was burning low,
and scarcely thinking, I put on a little coal. The noise of
this brought him up at once, and he stood aglare. He
peered about the room and was within an ace of touch-

---

10 **alertness:** Wachsamkeit.
11 **to strangle** (fig.): unterdrücken.
27 **to stand aglare:** mit wildem, durchdringendem Blick dastehen.
28f. **was within an ace of touching me:** hätte mich um ein Haar berührt.

ing me. Even after that examination, he scarcely seemed satisfied. He stopped in the doorway and took a final inspection before he went down.

I waited in the little parlour for an age, and at last he came up and opened the upstairs door. I just managed to get by him.

On the staircase he stopped suddenly, so that I very nearly blundered into him. He stood looking back right into my face and listening. 'I could have sworn,' he said. His long hairy hand pulled at his lower lip. His eye went up and down the staircase. Then he grunted and went on up again.

His hand was on the handle of a door, and then he stopped again with the same puzzled anger on his face. He was becoming aware of the faint sounds of my movements about him. The man must have had diabolically acute hearing. He suddenly flashed into rage. 'If there's anyone in this house,' he cried with an oath, and left the threat unfinished. He put his hand in his pocket, failed to find what he wanted, and rushing past me went blundering noisily and pugnaciously downstairs. But I did not follow him. I sat on the head of the staircase until his return.

Presently he came up again, still muttering. He opened the door of the room, and before I could enter, slammed it in my face.

I resolved to explore the house, and spent some time in doing so as noiselessly as possible. The house was very

11 **to grunt:** grunzen; brummen.
16 **diabolically** (adv.): teuflisch, höllisch.
17 **acute:** scharf, genau, fein.
18 **oath:** Fluch.
21 **pugnaciously** (adv.): streitlustig, aggressiv.

old and tumble-down, damp so that the paper in the at-
tics was peeling from the walls, and rat-infested. Some of
the door handles were stiff and I was afraid to turn them.
Several rooms I did inspect were unfurnished, and
others were littered with theatrical lumber, bought second-hand, I judged, from its appearance. In one room
next to his I found a lot of old clothes. I began routing
among these, and in my eagerness forgot again the evident sharpness of his ears. I heard a stealthy footstep
and, looking up just in time, saw him peering in at the
tumbled heap and holding an old-fashioned revolver in
his hand. I stood perfectly still while he stared about
open-mouthed and suspicious. 'It must have been her,'
he said slowly. 'Damn her!'
He shut the door quietly, and immediately I heard the
key turn in the lock. Then his footsteps retreated. I realised abruptly that I was locked in. For a minute I did not
know what to do. I walked from door to window and
back, and stood perplexed. A gust of anger came upon
me. But I decided to inspect the clothes before I did anything further, and my first attempt brought down a pile
from an upper shelf. This brought him back, more sinister than ever. That time he actually touched me, jumped
back with amazement and stood astonished in the middle of the room.

1 **tumble-down:** baufällig.
1 f. **attic:** Dachgeschoß.
2 **to peel:** abblättern.
   rat-infested: voller Ratten.
5 **lumber:** Plunder, Kram.
7 **to rout:** wühlen, stöbern.
9 **stealthy:** verstohlen.
11 **tumbled:** wirr, unordentlich.
22 f. **sinister:** drohend, finster.

Presently he calmed a little. 'Rats,' he said in an undertone, fingers on lip. He was evidently a little scared. I
edged quietly out of the room, but a plank creaked.
Then the infernal little brute started going all over the
5 house, revolver in hand and locking door after door and
pocketing the keys. When I realised what he was up to I
had a fit of rage – I could hardly control myself suffi-
ciently to watch my opportunity. By this time I knew he
was alone in the house, and so I made no more ado, but
10 knocked him on the head."

"Knocked him on the head!" exclaimed Kemp.

"Yes – stunned him – as he was going downstairs. Hit
him from behind with a stool that stood on the landing.
He went downstairs like a bag of old boots."

15 "But –! I say! The common conventions of humanity —"

"Are all very well for common people. But the point
was, Kemp, that I had to get out of that house in a disguise without his seeing me. I couldn't think of any other
20 way of doing it. And then I gagged him with a Louis
Quatorze vest and tied him up in a sheet."

"Tied him up in a sheet!"

"Made a sort of bag of it. It was rather a good idea to
keep the idiot scared and quiet, and a devilish hard
25 thing to get out of – head away from the string. My
dear Kemp, it's no good your sitting and glaring as
though I was a murderer. It had to be done. He had his

---

4 **brute:** Kerl.
9 **ado:** Umstände, Aufhebens.
20 **to gag:** knebeln.
20f. **Louis Quatorze** (Fr.): Ludwig XIV. (1638–1715), französischer Kö-
nig (seit 1643); (fig.): im Stil der Epoche Ludwigs XIV.

revolver. If once he saw me he would be able to describe me —"

"But still," said Kemp, "in England – to-day. And the man was in his own house, and you were – well, robbing."

"Robbing! Confound it! You'll call me a thief next! Surely, Kemp, you're not fool enough to dance on the old strings. Can't you see my position?"

"And his too," said Kemp.

The Invisible Man stood up sharply. "What do you mean to say?"

Kemp's face grew a trifle hard. He was about to speak and checked himself. "I suppose, after all," he said with a sudden change of manner, "the thing had to be done. You were in a fix. But still —"

"Of course I was in a fix – an infernal fix. And he made me wild too – hunting me about the house, fooling about with his revolver, locking and unlocking doors. He was simply exasperating. You don't blame me, do you? You don't blame me?"

"I never blame anyone," said Kemp. "It's quite out of fashion. What did you do next?"

"I was hungry. Downstairs I found a loaf and some rank cheese – more than sufficient to satisfy my hunger. I took some brandy and water, and then went up past my impromptu bag – he was lying quite still – to the room containing the old clothes. This looked out upon the street, two lace curtains brown with dirt guarding the window. I

---

7 f. **to dance on the old strings** (pl.): (fig.) nach der alten Pfeife tanzen.
15 **to be in a fix** (infml.): in der Klemme sitzen.
23 **rank**: ranzig, stinkend.
25 f. **impromptu** (Fr.): improvisiert.

went and peered out through their interstices. Outside
the day was bright – by contrast with the brown shadows
of the dismal house in which I found myself, dazzlingly
bright. A brisk traffic was going by, fruit carts, a hansom,
5 a four-wheeler with a pile of boxes, a fishmonger's cart.
I turned with spots of colour swimming before my eyes
to the shadowy fixtures behind me. My excitement was
giving place to a clear apprehension of my position
again. The room was full of a faint scent of benzoline,
10 used, I suppose, in cleaning the garments.
  I began a systematic search of the place. I should judge
the hunchback had been alone in the house for some
time. He was a curious person. Everything that could
possibly be of service to me I collected in the clothes
15 store-room, and then I made a deliberate selection. I
found a handbag I thought a suitable possession, and
some powder, rouge, and sticking-plaster.
  I had thought of painting and powdering my face and all
that there was to show of me, in order to render myself
20 visible, but the disadvantage of this lay in the fact that I
should require turpentine and other appliances and a
considerable amount of time before I could vanish
again. Finally I chose a mask of the better type, slightly
grotesque but not more so than many human beings,
25 dark glasses, greyish whiskers, and a wig. I could find no
underclothing, but that I could buy subsequently, and for

---

5 **fishmonger:** Fischhändler.
8 **apprehension** (arch.): Erkennen.
9 **benzoline:** Leichtbenzin.
12 **hunchback:** Buckeliger.
15 **deliberate:** sorgfältig, überlegt.
17 **rouge** (Fr.): rote Schminke.
21 **turpentine:** Terpentin.

the time I swathed myself in calico dominoes and some white cashmere scarfs. I could find no socks, but the hunchback's boots were rather a loose fit and sufficed. In a desk in the shop were three sovereigns and about
5 thirty shillings' worth of silver, and in a locked cupboard I burst in the inner room were eight pounds in gold. I could go forth into the world again, equipped.

Then came a curious hesitation. Was my appearance really – credible? I tried myself with a little bedroom
10 looking-glass, inspecting myself from every point of view to discover any forgotten chink, but it all seemed sound. I was grotesque to the theatrical pitch, a stage miser, but I was certainly not a physical impossibility. Gathering confidence, I took my looking-glass down into the
15 shop, pulled down the shop blinds, and surveyed myself from every point of view with the help of the cheval glass in the corner.

I spent some minutes screwing up my courage and then unlocked the shop door and marched out into the street,
20 leaving the little man to get out of his sheet again when he liked. In five minutes a dozen turnings intervened between me and the costumier's shop. No one appeared to notice me very pointedly. My last difficulty seemed overcome."

25 He stopped again.

"And you troubled no more about the hunchback?" said Kemp.

"No," said the Invisible Man. "Nor have I heard what

---

1 **calico:** Kattun.
11 **chink:** Ritze, Spalt.
12f. **miser:** Geizkragen.
21 **to intervene:** dazwischenliegen.
23 **pointedly** (adv.): auffallend, besonders.

became of him. I suppose he untied himself or kicked himself out. The knots were pretty tight."

He became silent, and went to the window and stared out.

5 "What happened when you went out into the Strand?"

"Oh! – disillusionment again. I thought my troubles were over. Practically I thought I had impunity to do whatever I chose, everything – save to give away my se-
10 cret. So I thought. Whatever I did, whatever the consequences might be, was nothing to me. I had merely to fling aside my garments and vanish. No person could hold me. I could take my money where I found it. I decided to treat myself to a sumptuous feast, and then put
15 up at a good hotel, and accumulate a new outfit of property. I felt amazingly confident, – it's not particularly pleasant recalling that I was an ass. I went into a place and was already ordering a lunch, when it occurred to me that I could not eat unless I exposed my invisible
20 face. I finished ordering the lunch, told the man I should be back in ten minutes, and went out exasperated. I don't know if you have ever been disappointed in your appetite."

"Not quite so badly," said Kemp, "but I can imagine
25 it."

"I could have smashed the silly devils. At last, faint with

---

7 **disillusionment:** Enttäuschung.
14 **to treat o.s. to s.th.:** sich etwas leisten, gönnen.
   sumptuous: üppig, verschwenderisch.
   feast: Festessen.
14f. **to put up at a hotel:** in einem Hotel absteigen, einkehren.
15 **to accumulate:** sammeln, zusammentragen.
17 **to recall:** sich erinnern.

the desire for tasteful food, I went into another place and demanded a private room. 'I am disfigured,' I said. 'Badly.' They looked at me curiously, but of course it was not their affair – and so at last I got my lunch. It was not particularly well served, but it sufficed; and when I had had it, I sat over a cigar, trying to plan my line of action. And outside a snowstorm was beginning.

The more I thought it over, Kemp, the more I realised what a helpless absurdity an Invisible Man was, – in a cold and dirty climate and a crowded civilised city. Before I made this mad experiment I had dreamt of a thousand advantages. That afternoon it seemed all disappointment. I went over the heads of the things a man reckons desirable. No doubt invisibility made it possible to get them, but it made it impossible to enjoy them when they are got. Ambition – what is the good of pride of place when you cannot appear there? What is the good of the love of woman when her name must needs be Delilah? I have no taste for politics, for the blackguardisms of fame, for philanthropy, for sport. What was I to do? And for this I had become a wrapped-up mystery, a swathed and bandaged caricature of a man!"

He paused, and his attitude suggested a roving glance at the window.

---

13 **head:** Rubrik.
14 **ro reckon:** (als etwas) ansehen, betrachten.
18 **needs** (adv.): ausgerechnet, unbedingt.
19 **Delilah:** Gestalt aus der Bibel; liebte Samson, den mit übermenschlichen Kräften ausgestatteten Helden aus dem israelitischen Stamm der Dan, und verriet ihn an die Philister.
19f. **blackguardism** (arch.): schurkische Verhaltensweise, Gemeinheit.
20 **philanthropy:** Menschenliebe.
23 **to rove:** schweifen (Blick).

"But how did you get to Iping?" said Kemp, anxious to keep his guest busy talking.

"I went there to work. I had one hope. It was a half idea! I have it still. It is a full blown idea now. A way of getting
5   back! Of restoring what I have done. When I choose. When I have done all I mean to do invisibly. And that is what I chiefly want to talk to you about now."

"You went straight to Iping?"

"Yes. I had simply to get my three volumes of memo-
10   randa and my cheque-book, my luggage and underclothing, order a quantity of chemicals to work out this idea of mine, – I will show you the calculations as soon as I get my books, – and then I started. Jove! I remember the snowstorm now, and the accursed bother it was to keep
15   the snow from damping my pasteboard nose."

"At the end," said Kemp, "the day before yesterday, when they found you out, you rather – to judge by the papers —"

"I did. Rather. Did I kill that fool of a constable?"

20   "No," said Kemp. "He's expected to recover."

"That's his luck, then. I clean lost my temper, the fools! Why couldn't they leave me alone? And that grocer lout?"

"There are no deaths expected," said Kemp.

25   "I don't know about that tramp of mine," said the Invisible Man, with an unpleasant laugh.

---

13 **Jove!** (auch: *by Jove*): Himmel!, Donnerwetter! (wörtl.: beim Jupiter!).
14 **accursed** (infml.): verflucht.
    bother: Plage.
15 **pasteboard nose:** Pappnase.
21 **clean** (adv.): glatt.
23 **lout:** Rüpel, Flegel.

"By Heaven, Kemp, you don't know what rage *is!* To have worked for years, to have planned and plotted, and then to get some fumbling purblind idiot messing across your course! Every conceivable sort of silly creature that has ever been created has been sent to cross me. If I have much more of it, I shall go wild, – I shall start mowing 'em.
As it is, they've made things a thousand times more difficult."

"No doubt it's exasperating," said Kemp, drily.

Chapter XXIV

The Plan that Failed

"But now," said Kemp, with a side glance out of the window, "what are we to do?"
He moved nearer his guest as he spoke in such a manner as to prevent the possibility of a glimpse of the three men who were advancing up the hill road – with an intolerable slowness, as it seemed to Kemp.
"What were you planning to do when you were heading for Port Burdock? *Had* you any plan?"
"I was going to clear out of the country. But I have altered that plan rather since seeing you. I thought it

---

3 **purblind** (fml.): dumm, kurzsichtig.
  to mess across s.th.: sich in etwas einmischen, etwas durcheinanderbringen.
7 **to mow:** niedermähen.
17 f. **intolerable:** unerträglich.

would be wise, now the weather is hot and invisibility possible, to make for the South. Especially as my secret was known, and everyone would be on the lookout for a masked and muffled man. You have a line of steamers
5 from here to France. My idea was to get aboard one and run the risks of the passage. Thence I could go by train into Spain, or else get to Algiers. It would not be difficult. There a man might always be invisible – and yet live. And do things. I was using that tramp as a money
10 box and luggage carrier, until I decided how to get my books and things sent over to meet me."

"That's clear."

"And then the filthy brute must needs try and rob me! He has hidden my books, Kemp. Hidden my books! If I
15 can lay my hands on him!"

"Best plan to get the books out of him first."

"But where is he? Do you know?"

"He's in the town police station, locked up, by his own request, in the strongest cell in the place."

20 "Cur!" said the Invisible Man.

"But that hangs up your plans a little."

"We must get those books; those books are vital."

"Certainly," said Kemp, a little nervously, wondering if he heard footsteps outside. "Certainly we must get those
25 books. But that won't be difficult, if he doesn't know they're for you."

"No," said the Invisible Man, and thought.

Kemp tried to think of something to keep the talk going, but the Invisible Man resumed of his own accord.

---

3 **to be on the lookout for s.o.:** nach jdm. Ausschau halten.
20 **cur:** (fig.) Hund, Halunke.
21 **to hang s.th. up:** etwas verzögern.

"Blundering into your house, Kemp," he said, "changes all my plans. For you are a man that can understand. In spite of all that has happened, in spite of this publicity, of the loss of my books, of what I have suffered, there still remain great possibilities, huge possibilities —"

"You have told no one I am here?" he asked abruptly.

Kemp hesitated. "That was implied," he said.

"No one?" insisted Griffin.

"Not a soul."

"Ah! Now –" The Invisible Man stood up, and sticking his arms akimbo began to pace the study.

"I made a mistake, Kemp, a huge mistake, in carrying this thing through alone. I have wasted strength, time, opportunities. Alone – it is wonderful how little a man can do alone! To rob a little, to hurt a little, and there is the end.

What I want, Kemp, is a goal-keeper, a helper, and a hiding-place, an arrangement whereby I can sleep and eat and rest in peace, and unsuspected. I must have a confederate. With a confederate, with food and rest – a thousand things are possible.

Hitherto I have gone on vague lines. We have to consider all that invisibility means, all that it does not mean. It means little advantage for eavesdropping and so forth – one makes sounds. It's of little help, a little help perhaps – in housebreaking and so forth. Once you've caught me you could easily imprison me. But on the other hand I am hard to catch. This invisibility, in fact, is only good in two cases: It's useful in getting away, it's

---

8 **to imply:** (stillschweigend) voraussetzen.
25 **eavesdropping:** Lauschen, heimliches Mithören.

useful in approaching. It's particularly useful, therefore, in killing. I can walk round a man, whatever weapon he has, choose my point, strike as I like. Dodge as I like. Escape as I like."

5 Kemp's hand went to his moustache. Was that a movement downstairs?

"And it is killing we must do, Kemp."

"It is killing we must do," repeated Kemp. "I'm listening to your plan, Griffin, but I'm not agreeing, mind. *Why*
10 killing?"

"Not wanton killing, but a judicious slaying. The point is, they know there is an Invisible Man – as well as we know there is an Invisible Man. And that Invisible Man, Kemp, must now establish a Reign of Terror. Yes – no
15 doubt it's startling. But I mean it. A Reign of Terror. He must take some town like your Burdock and terrify and dominate it. He must issue his orders. He can do that in a thousand ways – scraps of paper thrust under doors would suffice. And all who disobey his orders he
20 must kill, and kill all who would defend the disobedient."

"Humph!" said Kemp, no longer listening to Griffin but to the sound of his front door opening and closing.

"It seems to me, Griffin," he said, to cover his wander-
25 ing attention, "that your confederate would be in a difficult position."

"No one would know he was a confederate," said the In-

---

9 **mind:** wohlgemerkt.
11 **wanton:** mutwillig.
   judicious: wohlüberlegt.
17 **to issue:** (Befehl) erteilen.
22 **humph!:** hm! (Ausruf zum Ausdruck des Zweifels).
24f. **wandering attention:** nachlassende Aufmerksamkeit.

visible Man, eagerly. And the suddenly, "*Hush!* What's that downstairs?"

"Nothing," said Kemp, and suddenly began to speak loud and fast. "I don't agree to this, Griffin," he said. "Understand me, I don't agree to this. Why dream of playing a game against the race? How can you hope to gain happiness? Don't be a lone wolf. Publish your results; take the world – take the nation at least – into your confidence. Think what you might do with a million helpers —"

The Invisible Man interrupted Kemp. "There are footsteps coming upstairs," he said in a low voice.

"Nonsense," said Kemp.

"Let me see," said the Invisible Man, and advanced, arm extended, to the door.

Kemp hesitated for a second and then moved to intercept him. The Invisible Man started and stood still. "Traitor!" cried the Voice, and suddenly the dressing-gown opened, and sitting down the Unseen began to disrobe. Kemp made three swift steps to the door, and forthwith the Invisible Man – his legs had vanished – sprang to his feet with a shout. Kemp flung the door open.

As it opened, there came a sound of hurrying feet downstairs and voices.

With a quick movement Kemp thrust the Invisible Man back, sprang aside, and slammed the door. The key was outside and ready. In another moment Griffin would have been alone in the belvedere study, a prisoner. Save

---

7 **lone wolf** (fig.): Einzelgänger, Eigenbrödler.

8f. **to take s.o. into one's confidence:** jdn. ins Vertrauen ziehen.

19f. **to disrobe** (fml.): (Kleider) ablegen.

for one little thing. The key had been slipped in hastily
that morning. As Kemp slammed the door it fell noisily
upon the carpet.

Kemp's face became white. He tried to grip the door
5 handle with both hands. For a moment he stood lugging.
Then the door gave six inches. But he got it closed again.
The second time it was jerked a foot wide, and the dressing-gown came wedging itself into the opening. His
throat was gripped by invisible fingers, and he left his
10 hold on the handle to defend himself. He was forced
back, tripped and pitched heavily into the corner of the
landing. The empty dressing-gown was flung on the top
of him.

Halfway up the staircase was Colonel Adye, the recipi-
15 ent of Kemp's letter, the chief of the Burdock police. He
was staring aghast at the sudden appearance of Kemp,
followed by the extraordinary sight of clothing tossing
empty in the air. He saw Kemp felled, and struggling to
his feet. He saw him rush forward, and go down again,
20 felled like an ox.

Then suddenly he was struck violently. By nothing! A
vast weight, it seemed, leapt upon him, and he was
hurled headlong down the staircase, with the grip at his
throat and a knee in his groin. An invisible foot trod on
25 his back, a ghostly patter passed downstairs, he heard
the two police officers in the hall shout and run, and the
front door of the house slammed violently.

6 **to give:** nachgeben.
8 **to wedge o.s.:** sich klemmen, zwängen.
14f. **recipient:** Empfänger.
16 **aghast:** entgeistert.
24 **groin:** Leiste(ngegend), Unterleib.
25 **patter:** Getrappel.

He rolled over and sat up staring. He saw, staggering down the staircase, Kemp, dusty and dishevelled, one side of his face white from a blow, his lip bleeding, holding a pink dressing-gown and some underclothing in his arms.

"My God!" cried Kemp, "the game's up! He's gone!"

Chapter XXV

The Hunting of the Invisible Man

For a space Kemp was too inarticulate to make Adye understand the swift things that had just happened. The two men stood on the landing, Kemp speaking swiftly, the grotesque swathings of Griffin still on his arm. But presently Adye began to grasp something of the situation.

"He is mad," said Kemp; "inhuman. He is pure selfishness. He thinks of nothing but his own advantage, his own safety. I have listened to such a story this morning of brutal self-seeking! He has wounded men. He will kill them unless we can prevent him. He will create a panic. Nothing can stop him. He is going out now – furious!"

"He must be caught," said Adye. "That is certain."

"But how?" cried Kemp, and suddenly became full of

---

6 **the game's up:** das Spiel ist aus.
9 **to be inarticulate:** nicht in der Lage sein, sich auszudrücken.
12 **swathing:** Hülle.
18 **self-seeking:** Selbstsucht.

ideas. "You must begin at once. You must set every
available man to work. You must prevent his leaving
this district. Once he gets away, he may go through the
countryside as he wills, killing and maiming. He dreams
5 of a reign of terror! A reign of terror, I tell you. You
must set a watch on trains and roads and shipping. The
garrison must help. You must wire for help. The only
thing that may keep him here is the thought of recovering some books of notes he counts of value. I will tell
10 you of that! There is a man in your police station, –
Marvel."

"I know," said Adye, "I know. Those books – yes."

"And you must prevent him from eating or sleeping; day
and night the country must be astir for him. Food must
15 be locked up and secured, all food, so that he will have
to break his way to it. The houses everywhere must be
barred against him. Heaven send us cold nights and rain!
The whole countryside must begin hunting and keep
hunting. I tell you, Adye, he is a danger, a disaster; un-
20 less he is pinned and secured, it is frightful to think of the
things that may happen."

"What else can we do?" said Adye. "I must go down at
once and begin organising. But why not come? Yes – you
come too! Come, and we must hold a sort of council of
25 war, – get Hopps to help – and the railway managers. By

---

4 **to maim:** verstümmeln.
6 **to set a watch on s.th.:** etwas bewachen lassen.
7 **garrison:** Garnison.
   to wire: telegraphieren.
9 **to count s.th. of value:** etwas für wertvoll halten.
14 **to be astir for s.o.:** hier: ständig hinter jdm. her sein.
20 **to pin s.o.:** (fig.) jdn. festnageln.
24f. **council of war:** Kriegsrat.

Jove! it's urgent. Come along – tell me as we go. What else is there we can do? Put that stuff down."

In another moment Adye was leading the way downstairs. They found the front door open and the policemen standing outside staring at empty air. "He's got away, sir," said one.

"We must go to the central station at once," said Adye. "One of you go on down and get a cab to come up and meet us – quickly. And now, Kemp, what else?"

"Dogs." said Kemp. "Get dogs. They don't see him, but they wind him. Get dogs."

"Good," said Adye. "It's not generally known, but the prison officials over at Halstead know a man with bloodhounds. Dogs. What else?"

"Bear in mind," said Kemp, "his food shows. After eating, his food shows until it is assimilated. So that he has to hide after eating. You must keep on beating, – every thicket, every quiet corner. And put all weapons, all implements that might be weapons, away. He can't carry such things for long. And what he can snatch up and strike men with must be hidden away."

"Good again," said Adye. "We shall have him yet!"

"And on the roads," said Kemp, and hesitated.

"Yes?" said Adye.

"Powdered glass," said Kemp. "It's cruel, I know. But think of what he may do!"

Adye drew the air in between his teeth sharply. "It's unsportsmanlike. I don't know. But I'll have powdered glass got ready. If he goes too far —"

17 **to beat:** (Gebüsch o. ä.) durchstöbern.
18 f. **implement:** Werkzeug.
27 f. **unsportsmanlike:** unfair.

"The man's become inhuman, I tell you," said Kemp. "I am as sure he will establish a reign of terror – so soon as he has got over the emotions of this escape – as I am sure I am talking to you. Our only chance is to be ahead. He has cut himself off from his kind. His blood be upon his own head."

Chapter XXVI

The Wicksteed Murder

The Invisible Man seems to have rushed out of Kemp's house in a state of blind fury. A little child playing near Kemp's gateway was violently caught up and thrown aside, so that its ankle was broken, and thereafter for some hours the Invisible Man passed out of human perceptions. No one knows where he went nor what he did. But one can imagine him hurrying through the hot June forenoon, up the hill and on to the open downland behind Port Burdock, raging and despairing at his intolerable fate, and sheltering at last, heated and weary, amid the thickets of Hintondean, to piece together again his shattered schemes against his species. That seems the most probable refuge for him, for there it was he reasserted himself in a grimly tragical manner about two in the afternoon.

---

11 **gateway:** Einfahrt.
16 **downland:** (baumloses) Hügelland.
20 **shattered** (fig.): zunichte gemacht, zerschlagen.
   species: Spezies, Art; hier: Mitmenschen.
21 f. **to re-assert o.s.:** sich wieder behaupten, wieder erholen.

One wonders what his state of mind may have been during that time, and what plans he devised. No doubt he was almost ecstatically exasperated by Kemp's treachery, and though we may be able to understand the motives that led to that deceit, we may still imagine and even sympathise a little with the fury the attempted surprise must have occasioned. Perhaps something of the stunned astonishment of his Oxford Street experiences may have returned to him, for evidently he had counted on Kemp's co-operation in his brutal dream of a terrorised world. At any rate he vanished from human ken about midday, and no living witness can tell what he did until about half-past two. It was a fortunate thing, perhaps, for humanity, but for him it was a fatal inaction.

During that time a growing multitude of men scattered over the countryside were busy. In the morning he had still been simply a legend, a terror; in the afternoon, by virtue chiefly of Kemp's drily worded proclamation, he was presented as a tangible antagonist, to be wounded, captured, or overcome, and the countryside began organising itself with inconceivable rapidity. By two o'clock even he might still have removed himself out of the district by getting aboard a train, but after two that

---

1 **state of mind:** geistiger Zustand, seelische Verfassung.
2 **to devise s.th.:** etwas ersinnen.
4 **treachery:** Verrat.
5 **deceit:** Täuschung, Betrug.
7 **to occasion:** verursachen.
12 **ken:** Gesichtskreis.
18f. **by virtue of s.th.** (fml.): vermittels, auf Grund von etwas.
19 **to word:** in Worte fassen, formulieren.
20 **antagonist:** Gegner.

became impossible. Every passenger train along the
lines on a great parallelogram between Southampton,
Manchester, Brighton, and Horsham, travelled with
locked doors, and the goods traffic was almost entirely
5 suspended. And in a great circle of twenty miles round
Port Burdock, men armed with guns and bludgeons
were presently setting out in groups of three and four,
with dogs, to beat the roads and fields.

Mounted policemen rode along the country lanes, stop-
10 ping at every cottage and warning the people to lock up
their houses, and keep indoors unless they were armed,
and all the elementary schools had broken up by three
o'clock, and the children, scared and keeping together in
groups, were hurrying home. Kemp's proclamation –
15 signed indeed by Adye – was posted over almost the
whole district by four or five o'clock in the afternoon. It
gave briefly but clearly all the conditions of the struggle,
the necessity of keeping the Invisible Man from food
and sleep, the necessity for incessant watchfulness and
20 for a prompt attention to any evidence of his movements. And so swift and decided was the action of the
authorities, so prompt and universal was the belief in
this strange being, that before nightfall an area of several hundred square miles was in a stringent state of
25 siege. And before nightfall, too, a thrill of horror went
through the whole watching nervous countryside. Going
from whispering mouth to mouth, swift and certain over

---

5 **to suspend s.th.:** etwas aussetzen, einstellen.
6 **bludgeon:** Knüppel.
19 **incessant:** ständig, ununterbrochen.
24 **stringent:** streng, scharf.
24f. **state of siege:** Belagerungszustand.

the length and breadth of the county, passed the story of the murder of Mr. Wicksteed.

If our supposition that the Invisible Man's refuge was the Hintondean thickets, then we must suppose that in the early afternoon he sallied out again bent upon some project that involved the use of a weapon. We cannot know what the project was, but the evidence that he had the iron rod in hand before he met Wicksteed is to me at least overwhelming.

We can know nothing of the details of the encounter. It occurred on the edge of a gravel pit, not two hundred yards from Lord Burdock's Lodge gate. Everything points to a desperate struggle, – the trampled ground, the numerous wounds Mr. Wicksteed received, his splintered walking-stick; but why the attack was made – save in a murderous frenzy – it is impossible to imagine. Indeed the theory of madness is almost unavoidable. Mr. Wicksteed was a man of forty-five or forty-six, steward to Lord Burdock, of inoffensive habits and appearance, the very last person in the world to provoke such a terrible antagonist. Against him it would seem the Invisible Man used an iron rod dragged from a broken piece of fence. He stopped this quiet man, going quietly home to his midday meal, attacked him, beat down his feeble de-

5 (*to be*) **bent upon s.th.:** zu etwas entschlossen sein.
8 **iron rod:** Eisenstange.
11 **gravel pit:** Kiesgrube.
12 **lodge gate:** Pförtnerhaustor.
14f. **splintered:** zersplittert.
16 **frenzy:** Raserei, Wut.
18 **steward:** Verwalter.
19 **inoffensive:** harmlos.

fences, broke his arm, felled him, and smashed his head
to a jelly.

He must have dragged this rod out of the fencing before
he met his victim; he must have been carrying it ready in
his hand. Only two details beyond what has already been
stated seem to bear on the matter. One is the circum-
stance that the gravel pit was not in Mr. Wicksteed's di-
rect path home, but nearly a couple of hundred yards out
of his way. The other is the assertion of a little girl to the
effect that, going to her afternoon school, she saw the
murdered man "*trotting*" in a peculiar manner across a
field towards the gravel pit. Her pantomime of his action
suggests a man pursuing something on the ground before him and striking at it ever and again with his walking-stick. She was the last person to see him alive. He
passed out of her sight to his death, the struggle being
hidden from her only by a clump of beech trees and a
slight depression in the ground.

Now this, to the present writer's mind at least, lifts the
murder out of the realm of the absolutely wanton. We
may imagine that Griffin had taken the rod as a weapon
indeed, but without any deliberate intention of using it
in murder. Wicksteed may then have come by and noticed this rod inexplicably moving through the air. Without any thought of the Invisible Man – for Port Burdock
is ten miles away – he may have pursued it. It is quite
conceivable that he may not even have heard of the In-

6 **to bear on s.th.:** etwas betreffen, für etwas von Belang sein.
9 **assertion:** Behauptung.
9f. **to the effect that** (fml.): des Inhalts, daß …
17 **clump:** (Baum-)Gruppe.
18 **depression:** Vertiefung, Senke.
20 **realm:** (fig.) Reich.

visible Man. One can then imagine the Invisible Man
making off – quietly in order to avoid discovering his
presence in the neighbourhood, and Wicksteed, excited
and curious, pursuing this unaccountably locomotive
object, – finally striking at it.

No doubt the Invisible Man could easily have distanced
his middle-aged pursuer under ordinary circumstances,
but the position in which Wicksteed's body was found
suggests that he had the ill luck to drive his quarry into a
corner between a drift of stinging nettles and the gravel
pit. To those who appreciate the extraordinary irascibility of the Invisible Man, the rest of the encounter will be
easy to imagine.

But this is pure hypothesis. The only undeniable facts –
for stories of children are often unreliable – are the discovery of Wicksteed's body, done to death, and of the
blood-stained iron rod flung among the nettles. The
abandonment of the rod by Griffin suggests that in the
emotional excitement of the affair the purpose for which
he took it – if he had a purpose – was abandoned. He was
certainly an intensely egotistical and unfeeling man, but
the sight of his victim, his first victim, bloody and pitiful
at his feet, may have released some long pent fountain of

4 **locomotive:** sich fortbewegend.
6 f. **to distance s.o.:** jdn. hinter sich lassen.
9 **quarry:** Beute.
10 **drift:** Anhäufung.
   nettle: Brennessel.
11 f. **irascibility:** Reizbarkeit.
15 **unreliable:** unzuverlässig.
16 **done to death:** zu Tode gebracht, getötet.
18 **abandonment:** hier: Wegwerfen.
21 **egotistical:** egoistisch.
23 **pent:** aufgestaut.

remorse to flood for a time whatever scheme of action
he had contrived.

After the murder of Mr. Wicksteed, he would seem to
have struck across the country towards the downland.
5 There is a story of a voice heard about sunset by a couple
of men in a field near Fern Bottom. It was wailing and
laughing, sobbing and groaning, and ever and again it
shouted. It must have been queer hearing. It drove up
across the middle of a clover field and died away to-
10 wards the hills.

That afternoon the Invisible Man must have learnt
something of the rapid use Kemp had made of his confidences. He must have found houses locked and secured; he may have loitered about railway stations and
15 prowled about inns, and no doubt he read the procla-
mations and realised something of the nature of the
campaign against him. And as the evening advanced,
the fields became dotted here and there with groups of
three or four men, and noisy with the yelping of dogs.
20 These men-hunters had particular instructions as to the
way they should support one another in the case of an
encounter. He avoided them all. We may understand
something of his exasperation, and it could have been
none the less because he himself had supplied the in-

---

1 **remorse:** Reue, Gewissensbisse.
2 **to contrive s.th.:** etwas ersinnen, entwickeln.
4 **to strike:** (Weg, Richtung) einschlagen.
6 **to wail:** klagen, jammern.
9 **clover:** Klee.
12 f. **confidences:** vertrauliche Mitteilungen.
14 **to loiter:** sich herumtreiben.
18 **dotted:** gesprenkelt, übersät.
23 f. **could have been none the less:** konnte nicht verringert worden sein.

formation that was being used so remorselessly against him. For that day at least he lost heart; for nearly twenty-four hours, save when he turned on Wicksteed, he was a hunted man. In the night, he must have eaten and slept; for in the morning he was himself again, active, powerful, angry, and malignant, prepared for his last great struggle against the world.

Chapter XXVII

The Siege of Kemp's House

Kemp read a strange missive, written in pencil on a greasy sheet of paper.

"You have been amazingly energetic and clever," this . letter ran, "though what you stand to gain by it I cannot imagine. You are against me. For a whole day you have chased me; you have tried to rob me of a night's rest. But I have had food in spite of you, I have slept in spite of you, and the game is only beginning. The game is only beginning. There is nothing for it, but to start the Terror. This announces the first day of the Terror. Port Burdock is no longer under the Queen, tell your Colonel of Police, and the rest of them; it is under me – the Terror! This is day one of year one of the new epoch, – the

---

1 **remorselessly** (adv.): unbarmherzig.
6 **malignant:** boshaft, bösartig.
10 **missive** (fml.): Botschaft, Brief.
13 **what you stand to gain by it:** was Sie dadurch zu gewinnen erhoffen.

Epoch of the Invisible Man. I am Invisible Man the First.
To begin with the rule will be easy. The first day there
will be one execution for the sake of example, – a man
named Kemp. Death starts for him to-day. He may lock
5 himself away, hide himself away, get guards about him,
put on armour if he likes; Death, the unseen Death, is
coming. Let him take precautions; it will impress my
people. Death starts from the pillar box by midday. The
letter will fall in as the postman comes along, then off!
10 The game begins. Death starts. Help him not, my people, lest Death fall upon you also. To-day Kemp is to
die."
Kemp read this letter twice. "It's no hoax," he said.
"That's his voice! And he means it."
15 He turned the folded sheet over and saw on the addressed side of it the postmark Hintondean, and the prosaic detail "*2d. to pay.*"
He got up, leaving his lunch unfinished, – the letter had
come by the one o'clock post, – and went into his study.
20 He rang for his housekeeper, and told her to go round
the house at once, examine all the fastenings of the windows, and close all the shutters. He closed the shutters of
his study himself. From a locked drawer in his bedroom
he took a little revolver, examined it carefully, and put it
25 into the pocket of his lounge jacket. He wrote a number
of brief notes, one to Colonel Adye, gave them to his

---

3 **for the sake of example:** um ein Exempel zu statuieren.
6 **armour:** Rüstung.
7 **precautions:** Vorkehrungen, Vorsichtsmaßnahmen.
8 **pillar box** (BE): Briefkasten(säule).
16f. **prosaic:** alltäglich, nüchtern.
17 **d.:** Abk. für penny, pence (von lat. *denarius* ›je 10 enthaltend‹).
21 **fastening:** Verschluß, Riegel.

servant to take, with explicit instructions as to her way of leaving the house. "There is no danger," he said, and added a mental reservation, "to you." He remained meditative for a space after doing this, and then returned to his cooling lunch.

He ate with gaps of thought. Finally he struck the table sharply. "We will have him!" he said; "and I am the bait. He will come too far."

He went up to the belvedere, carefully shutting every door after him. "It's a game," he said, "an odd game – but the chances are all for me, Mr. Griffin, in spite of your invisibility. Griffin *contra mundum* – with a vengeance!"

He stood at the window staring at the hot hillside. "He must get food every day – and I don't envy him. Did he really sleep last night? Out in the open somewhere – secure from collisions. I wish we could get some good cold wet weather instead of the heat.

He may be watching me now."

He went close to the window. Something rapped smartly against the brickwork over the frame, and made him start violently.

"I'm getting nervous," said Kemp. But it was five minutes before he went to the window again. "It must have been a sparrow," he said.

Presently he heard the front-door bell ringing, and hur-

---

3 **reservation:** Vorbehalt.
4 **meditative:** nachdenklich.
7 **bait:** Köder.
12 **contra mundum** (Lat.): gegen die Welt.
12f. **with a vengeance:** 1. mit einer Rache, Vergeltung; 2. (infml.) gewaltig!
21 **brickwork:** Mauerwerk.

ried downstairs. He unbolted and unlocked the door, examined the chain, put it up, and opened cautiously without showing himself. A familiar voice hailed him. It was Adye.

5 "Your servant's been assaulted, Kemp," he said round the door.

"What!" exclaimed Kemp.

"Had that note of yours taken away from her. He's close about here. Let me in."

10 Kemp released the chain, and Adye entered through as narrow an opening as possible. He stood in the hall, looking with infinite relief at Kemp refastening the door. "Note was snatched out of her hand. Scared her horribly. She's down at the station. Hysterics. He's close here.

15 What was it about?"

Kemp swore.

"What a fool I was," said Kemp. "I might have known. It's not an hour's walk from Hintondean. Already!"

"What's up?" said Adye.

20 "Look here!" said Kemp, and led the way into his study. He handed Adye the Invisible Man's letter. Adye read it and whistled softly. "And you –?" said Adye.

"Proposed a trap – like a fool," said Kemp, "and sent my proposal out by a maid servant. To him."

25 Adye followed Kemp's profanity.

"He'll clear out," said Adye.

"Not he," said Kemp.

A resounding smash of glass came from upstairs. Adye had a silvery glimpse of a little revolver half out of

30 Kemp's pocket. "It's a window, upstairs!" said Kemp, and led the way up. There came a second smash while

25 **profanity:** Fluchen.

they were still on the staircase. When they reached the
study they found two of the three windows smashed, half
the room littered with splintered glass, and one big flint
lying on the writing table. The two men stopped in the
doorway, contemplating the wreckage. Kemp swore
again, and as he did so the third window went with a
snap like a pistol, hung starred for a moment, and col-
lapsed in jagged, shivering triangles into the room.

"What's this for?" said Adye.

"It's a beginning," said Kemp.

"There's no way of climbing up here?"

"Not for a cat," said Kemp.

"No shutters?"

"Not here. All the downstairs rooms – Hullo!"

Smash, and then whack of boards hit hard came from
downstairs. "Confound him!" said Kemp. "That must be
– yes – it's one of the bedrooms. He's going to do all the
house. But he's a fool. The shutters are up, and the glass
will fall outside. He'll cut his feet."

Another window proclaimed its destruction. The two
men stood on the landing perplexed. "I have it!" said
Adye. "Let me have a stick or something, and I'll go
down to the station and get the bloodhounds put on.
That ought to settle him! They're hard by – not ten minutes —"

Another window went the way of its fellows.

"You haven't a revolver?" asked Adye.

5 **wreckage:** hier: Zerstörungswerk.
8 **jagged:** gezackt, zackig.
15 **whack:** knallender Schlag.
20 **to proclaim:** (fig.) laut verkünden.
23 **to get the bloodhounds put on:** die Bluthunde auf die Spur setzen.
24 **to be hard by:** ganz nahe sein.

Kemp's hand went to his pocket. Then he hesitated. "I haven't one – at least to spare."

"I'll bring it back," said Adye, "you'll be safe here."

Kemp handed him the weapon.

5 "Now for the door," said Adye.

As they stood hesitating in the hall, they heard one of the first-floor bedroom windows crack and clash. Kemp went to the door and began to slip the bolts as silently as possible. His face was a little paler than

10 usual. "You must step straight out," said Kemp. In another moment Adye was on the doorstep and the bolts were dropping back into the staples. He hesitated for a moment, feeling more comfortable with his back against the door. Then he marched, upright and square,

15 down the steps. He crossed the lawn and approached the gate. A little breeze seemed to ripple over the grass. Something moved near him. "Stop a bit," said a Voice, and Adye stopped dead and his hand tightened on the revolver.

20 "Well?" said Adye, white and grim, and every nerve tense.

"Oblige me by going back to the house," said the Voice, as tense and grim as Adye's.

"Sorry," said Adye a little hoarsely, and moistened

25 his lips with his tongue. The Voice was on his left front, he thought. Suppose he were to take his luck with a shot?

---

14 **square:** fest.
16 **to ripple:** spielen, streichen, leicht wehen.
21 **tense:** angespannt.
22 **to oblige s.o. by doing s.th.:** jdm. die Güte erweisen, den Gefallen tun und etwas tun.
24 **to moisten:** befeuchten.

"What are you going for?" said the Voice, and there was a quick movement of the two, and a flash of sunlight from the open lip of Adye's pocket.

Adye desisted and thought. "Where I go," he said slowly, "is my own business." The words were still on his lips, when an arm came round his neck, his back felt a knee, and he was sprawling backward. He drew clumsily and fired absurdly, and in another moment he was struck in the mouth and the revolver wrested from his grip. He made a vain clutch at a slippery limb, tried to struggle up and fell back. "Damn!" said Adye. The Voice laughed. "I'd kill you now if it wasn't the waste of a bullet," it said. He saw the revolver in mid-air, six feet off, covering him.

"Well?" said Adye, sitting up.

"Get up," said the Voice.

Adye stood up.

"Attention," said the Voice, and then fiercely, "Don't try any games. Remember I can see your face if you can't see mine. You've got to go back to the house."

"He won't let me in," said Adye.

"That's a pity," said the Invisible Man. "I've got no quarrel with you."

Adye moistened his lips again. He glanced away from the barrel of the revolver and saw the sea far off very blue and dark under the midday sun, the smooth green down, the white cliff of the Head, and the multitudinous

---

3 **lip:** Rand, Saum.
4 **to desist:** innehalten, (von etwas) ablassen.
9 **to wrest:** entwinden, -reißen.
13 **to cover s.o.:** auf jdn. zielen, jdn. in Schach halten.
26 **Head:** gemeint ist vermutl. *Beachy Head:* steil ins Meer abfallendes Kap in den Southern Downs von Sussex, zwischen Hastings und Brighton gelegen.
   multitudinous: hier: belebt.

town, and suddenly he knew that life was very sweet. His
eyes came back to this little metal thing hanging between heaven and earth, six yards away. "What am I to
do?" he said sullenly.

5 "What am *I* to do?" asked the Invisible Man. "You will
get help. The only thing is for you to go back."

"I will try. If he lets me in will you promise not to rush
the door?"

"I've got no quarrel with you," said the Voice.

10 Kemp had hurried upstairs after letting Adye out, and
now crouching among the broken glass and peering cautiously over the edge of the study window sill, he saw
Adye stand parleying with the Unseen. "Why doesn't he
fire?" whispered Kemp to himself. Then the revolver
15 moved a little and the glint of the sunlight flashed in
Kemp's eyes. He shaded his eyes and tried to see the
source of the blinding beam.

"Surely!" he said, "Adye has given up the revolver."

"Promise not to rush the door," Adye was saying. "Don't
20 push a winning game too far. Give a man a chance."

"You go back to the house. I tell you flatly I will not
promise anything."

Adye's decision seemed suddenly made. He turned towards the house, walking slowly with his hands behind
25 him. Kemp watched him – puzzled. The revolver vanished, flashed again into sight, vanished again, and be-

---

4 **sullenly** (adv.): mürrisch.
7f. **to rush the door:** den Eingang erzwingen.
12 **window sill:** Fenstersims, -brett.
13 **to parley:** verhandeln.
15 **glint:** Funkeln, Glitzern, Schimmer.
21 **flatly** (adv.): rundweg, klar, deutlich.

came evident on a closer scrutiny as a little dark object
following Adye. Then things happened very quickly.
Adye leapt backwards, swung round, clutched at this little object, missed it, threw up his hands and fell forward
on his face, leaving a little puff of blue in the air. Kemp
did not hear the sound of the shot. Adye writhed, raised
himself on one arm, fell forward, and lay still.

For a space Kemp remained staring at the quiet careless-
ness of Adye's attitude. The afternoon was very hot and
still, nothing seemed stirring in all the world save a
couple of yellow butterflies chasing each other through
the shrubbery between the house and the road gate.
Adye lay on the lawn near the gate. The blinds of all the
villas down the hill-road were drawn, but in one little
green summer-house was a white figure, apparently an
old man asleep. Kemp scrutinised the surroundings of
the house for a glimpse of the revolver, but it had vanished. His eyes came back to Adye. The game was opening well.

Then came a ringing and knocking at the front door, that
grew at last tumultuous, but pursuant to Kemp's instructions the servants had locked themselves into their
rooms. This was followed by a silence. Kemp sat listening and then began peering cautiously out of the three
windows, one after another. He went to the staircase
head and stood listening uneasily. He armed himself
with his bedroom poker, and went to examine the interi-

---

 1 **scrutiny:** genaue Betrachtung.
 5 **puff:** Rauchwolke.
 6 **to writhe:** sich winden, krümmen.
12 **shrubbery:** Büsche, Sträucher.
21 **pursuant to** (fml.): gemäß.
26 **uneasily** (adv.): unbehaglich, mit Unbehagen.

or fastenings of the ground-floor windows again. Everything was safe and quiet. He returned to the belvedere. Adye lay motionless over the edge of the gravel just as he had fallen. Coming along the road by the villas were
5 the housemaid and two policemen.

Everything was deadly still. The three people seemed very slow in approaching. He wondered what his antagonist was doing.

He started. There was a smash from below. He hesitated
10 and went downstairs again. Suddenly the house resounded with heavy blows and the splintering of wood. He heard a smash and the destructive clang of the iron fastenings of the shutters. He turned the key and opened the kitchen door. As he did so, the shutters, split and
15 splintering, came flying inward. He stood aghast. The window frame, save for one cross bar, was still intact, but only little teeth of glass remained in the frame. The shutters had been driven in with an axe, and now the axe was descending in sweeping blows upon the window frame
20 and the iron bars defending it. Then suddenly it leapt aside and vanished. He saw the revolver lying on the path outside, and then the little weapon sprang into the air. He dodged back. The revolver cracked just too late, and a splinter from the edge of the closing door flashed
25 over his head. He slammed and locked the door, and as he stood outside he heard Griffin shouting and laughing. Then the blows of the axe with their splitting and smashing accompaniments, were resumed.

12 **clang:** Rasseln.
16 **cross bar:** Querstrebe.
19 **sweeping blows:** weit ausladende Schläge.
24 **splinter:** Splitter.

Kemp stood in the passage trying to think. In a moment the Invisible Man would be in the kitchen. This door would not keep him a moment, and then —

A ringing came at the front door again. It would be the policemen. He ran into the hall, put up the chain, and drew the bolts. He made the girl speak before he dropped the chain, and the three people blundered into the house in a heap, and Kemp slammed the door again.

"The Invisible Man!" said Kemp. "He has a revolver, with two shots – left. He's killed Adye. Shot him anyhow. Didn't you see him on the lawn? He's lying there."

"Who?" said one of the policemen.

"Adye," said Kemp.

"We came round the back way," said the girl.

"What's that smashing?" asked one of the policemen.

"He's in the kitchen – or will be. He has found an axe —"

Suddenly the house was full of the Invisible Man's resounding blows on the kitchen door. The girl stared towards the kitchen, shuddered, and retreated into the dining-room. Kemp tried to explain in broken sentences. They heard the kitchen door give.

"This way," cried Kemp, starting into activity, and bundled the policemen into the dining-room doorway.

"Poker," said Kemp, and rushed to the fender. He handed a poker to each policeman. He suddenly flung himself backward.

"Whup!" said one policeman, ducked, and caught the

25 **to bundle s.o. into s.th.:** jdn. in etwas hineindrängen.
30 **to catch:** abbekommen, erwischen.

axe on his poker. The pistol snapped its penultimate shot
and ripped a valuable Sidney Cooper. The second policeman brought his poker down on the little weapon, as
one might knock down a wasp, and sent it rattling to the
floor.

At the first clash the girl screamed, stood screaming for
a moment by the fireplace, and then ran to open the
shutters – possibly with an idea of escaping by the shattered window.

The axe receded into the passage, and fell to a position
about two feet from the ground. They could hear the Invisible Man breathing. "Stand away, you two," he said.
"I want that man Kemp."

"We want you," said the first policeman, making a quick
step forward and wiping with his poker at the Voice. The
Invisible Man must have started back. He blundered
into the umbrella stand. Then, as the policeman staggered with the swing of the blow he had aimed, the Invisible Man countered with the axe, the helmet crumpled like paper, and the blow sent the man spinning to
the floor at the head of the kitchen stairs. But the second
policeman, aiming behind the axe with his poker, hit
something soft that snapped. There was a sharp exclamation of pain and then the axe fell to the ground. The

---

1 **penultimate:** vorletzte(r, -s).
2 **to rip:** aufschlitzen.
  Cooper: Thomas Sidney C. (1803–1902), englischer Landschafts- und
  Tiermaler.
4 **wasp:** Wespe.
6 **clash:** Scheppern, Dröhnen; Zusammenstoß.
15 **to wipe at s.o.:** jdm. einen weit ausholenden Schlag versetzen.
19 **to counter:** kontern, parieren.
19f. **to crumple:** (zer)knittern.

policeman wiped again at vacancy and hit nothing; he put his foot on the axe, and struck again. Then he stood, poker clubbed, listening intent for the slightest movement.

He heard the dining-room window open, and a quick rush of feet within. His companion rolled over and sat up, with the blood running down between his eye and ear. "Where is he?" asked the man on the floor.

"Don't know. I've hit him. He's standing somewhere in the hall. Unless he's slipped past you. Doctor Kemp – sir."

Pause.

"Doctor Kemp," cried the policeman again.

The second policeman struggled to his feet. He stood up. Suddenly the faint pad of bare feet on the kitchen stairs could be heard. "Yap!" cried the first policeman, and incontinently flung his poker. It smashed a little gas bracket.

He made as if he would pursue the Invisible Man downstairs. Then he thought better of it and stepped into the dining-room.

"Doctor Kemp," he began, and stopped short —

"Doctor Kemp's in here," he said, as his companion looked over his shoulder.

The dining-room window was wide open, and neither housemaid nor Kemp was to be seen.

The second policeman's opinion of Kemp was terse and vivid.

---

1 **at vacancy:** ins Leere.
3 **poker clubbed:** etwa: den Feuerhaken schlagbereit in der Hand.
17f. **gas bracket:** an der Wand befestigter (Gas-)Lampenhalter.
20 **to think better of s.th:** sich eines Besseren besinnen.
27 **terse:** knapp, prägnant.

Chapter XXVIII

The Hunter Hunted

Mr. Heelas, Mr. Kemp's nearest neighbour among the
villa holders, was asleep in his summer-house when the
siege of Kemp's house began. Mr. Heelas was one of the
sturdy minority who refused to believe "in all this nonsense" about an Invisible Man. His wife, however, as he
was to be reminded subsequently, did. He insisted upon
walking about his garden just as if nothing was the matter, and he went to sleep in the afternoon in accordance
with the custom of years. He slept through the smashing
of the windows, and then woke up suddenly with a curious persuasion of something wrong. He looked across at
Kemp's house, rubbed his eyes and looked again. Then
he put his feet to the ground, and sat listening. He said
he was damned, and still the strange thing was visible.
The house looked as though it had been deserted for
weeks – after a violent riot. Every window was broken,
and every window, save those of the belvedere study,
was blinded by the internal shutters.
"I could have sworn it was all right" – he looked at his
watch – "twenty minutes ago."
He became aware of a measured concussion and the
clash of glass, far away in the distance. And then, as he
sat open-mouthed, came a still more wonderful thing.
The shutters of the drawing-room window were flung
open violently, and the housemaid in her outdoor hat
and garments, appeared struggling in a frantic manner to

---

6 **sturdy:** unerschütterlich, stur.
23 **measured:** regelmäßig, sich gleichmäßig wiederholend.

throw up the sash. Suddenly a man appeared beside her, helping her, – Doctor Kemp! In another moment the window was open, and the housemaid was struggling out; she pitched forward and vanished among the shrubs. Mr. Heelas stood up, exclaiming vaguely and vehemently at all these wonderful things. He saw Kemp stand on the sill, spring from the window, and reappear almost instantaneously running along a path in the shrubbery and stooping as he ran, like a man who evades observation. He vanished behind a laburnum, and appeared again clambering a fence that abutted on the open down. In a second he had tumbled over and was running at a tremendous pace down the slope towards Mr. Heelas.

"Lord!" cried Mr. Heelas, struck with an idea; "it's that Invisible Man brute! It's right, after all!"

With Mr. Heelas to think things like that was to act, and his cook watching him from the top window was amazed to see him come pelting towards the house at a good nine miles an hour. "Thought he wasn't afraid," said the cook. "Mary, just come here!" There was a slamming of doors, a ringing of bells, and the voice of Mr. Heelas bellowing like a bull. "Shut the doors, shut the windows, shut everything! the Invisible Man is coming!" Instantly the house was full of screams and directions, and scurry-

---

4 **to pitch forward:** kopfüber stürzen, fallen.
8 **instantaneously** (adv.): augenblicklich, unmittelbar.
9 **to evade s.th.:** sich einer Sache entziehen, einer Sache ausweichen.
10 **laburnum:** Goldregen (Zierstrauch).
11 f. **to abut on s.th.:** an etwas grenzen, stoßen.
19 **to pelt towards s.th.:** auf etwas zurasen.
22 f. **to bellow:** brüllen.
25 f. **to scurry:** huschen, hasten, eilig trippeln.

ing feet. He ran to shut the French windows himself that
opened on the veranda; as he did so Kemp's head and
shoulders and knee appeared over the edge of the garden fence. In another moment Kemp had ploughed
5 through the asparagus, and was running across the ten-
nis lawn to the house.

"You can't come in," said Mr. Heelas, shutting the
bolts. "I'm very sorry if he's after you, but you can't
come in!"

10 Kemp appeared with a face of terror close to the glass,
rapping and then shaking frantically at the French window. Then, seeing his efforts were useless, he ran along
the veranda, vaulted the end, and went to hammer at the
side door. Then he ran round by the side gate to the front
15 of the house, and so into the hill-road. And Mr. Heelas
staring from his window – a face of horror – had scarcely
witnessed Kemp vanish, ere the asparagus was being
trampled this way and that by feet unseen. At that Mr.
Heelas fled precipitately upstairs, and the rest of the
20 chase is beyond his purview. But as he passed the staircase window, he heard the side gate slam.

Emerging into the hill-road, Kemp naturally took the
downward direction, and so it was he came to run in his
own person the very race he had watched with such a
25 critical eye from the belvedere study only four days ago.

---

1 **French window:** Glastür nach draußen, Verandatür.
4f. **to plough through s.th.:** sich einen Weg durch etwas bahnen; durch
   etwas rasen.
5 **asparagus:** Spargel; hier: Spargelbeet.
13 **to vault s.th.:** sich über etwas schwingen, über etwas springen.
17 **ere** (arch.): bevor, ehe.
19 **precipitately** (adv.): überstürzt, eilig.
20 **purview** (fml.): Gesichtskreis.

He ran it well for a man out of training; and though his face was white and wet, his wits were cool to the last. He ran with wide strides, and wherever a patch of rough ground intervened, wherever there came a patch of raw flints, or a bit of broken glass shone dazzling, he crossed it and left the bare invisible feet that followed to take what line they would.

For the first time in his life Kemp discovered that the hill-road was indescribably vast and desolate, and that the beginnings of the town far below at the hill foot were strangely remote. Never had there been a slower or more painful method of progression than running. All the gaunt villas, sleeping in the afternoon sun, looked locked and barred; no doubt they were locked and barred – by his own orders. But at any rate they might have kept a lookout for an eventuality like this! The town was rising up now, the sea had dropped out of sight behind it, and people down below were stirring. A tram was just arriving at the hill foot. Beyond that was the police station. Was that footsteps he heard behind him? Spurt.

The people below were staring at him, one or two were running, and his breath was beginning to saw in his throat. The tram was quite near now, and the Jolly Cricketers was noisily barring its doors. Beyond the tram were posts and heaps of gravel, – the drainage works. He had a transitory idea of jumping into the tram

---

2 **his wits were cool:** er bewahrte einen kühlen Kopf.
13 **gaunt:** öde, verlassen (wirkend).
16 **eventuality:** möglicher Fall.
23 **to saw:** hier (fig.): sägen, schneiden.
26 **drainage:** Kanalisation.
27 **transitory:** vorübergehend.

and slamming the doors, and then he resolved to go for
the police station. In another moment he had passed the
door of the Jolly Cricketers, and was in the blistering fag
end of the street, with human beings about him. The
5 tram driver and his helper – arrested by the sight of his
furious haste – stood staring with the tram horses unhitched. Further on the astonished features of navvies
appeared above the mounds of gravel.

His pace broke a little, and then he heard the swift pad
10 of his pursuer, and leapt forward again. "The Invisible
Man!" he cried to the navvies, with a vague indicative
gesture, and by an inspiration leapt the excavation and
placed a burly group between him and the chase. Then
abandoning the idea of the police station he turned into
15 a little side street, rushed by a greengrocer's cart, hesitated for the tenth of a second at the door of a sweetstuff shop, and then made for the mouth of an alley
that ran back into the main Hill Street again. Two or
three little children were playing here, and shrieked
20 and scattered running at his apparition, and forthwith
doors and windows opened and excited mothers re-

---

3 f. **fag end** (infml.): äußerstes Ende.
6 f. **unhitched:** losgebunden.
7 **navvy:** Straßenarbeiter.
8 **mound:** Hügel, Haufen.
9 **his pace broke:** sein Tempo verlangsamte sich.
11 **indicative:** auf etwas hindeutend.
12 **excavation:** Graben.
15 **greengrocer:** Gemüsehändler.
17 **alley:** Gasse.
20 **to scatter:** auseinanderlaufen, -stieben.
 apparition: Erscheinen, Auftauchen.
21 f. **excited mothers revealed their hearts:** etwa: aufgeregte Mütter
 zeigten Entschlossenheit.

vealed their hearts. Out he shot into Hill Street again,
three hundred yards from the tram-line end, and immediately he became aware of a tumultuous vociferation
and running people.

He glanced up the street towards the hill. Hardly a
dozen yards off ran a huge navvy, cursing in fragments
and slashing viciously with a spade, and hard behind him
came the tram conductor with his fists clenched. Up the
street others followed these two, striking and shouting.
Down towards the town, men and women were running,
and he noticed clearly one man coming out of a shop-
door with a stick in his hand. "Spread out! Spread out!"
cried some one. Kemp suddenly grasped the altered condition of the chase. He stopped, and looked round, panting. "He's close here!" he cried. "Form a line across —"
"Aha!" shouted a voice.

He was hit hard under the ear, and went reeling, trying
to face round towards his unseen antagonist. He just
managed to keep his feet, and he struck a vain counter
in the air. Then he was hit again under the jaw, and
sprawled headlong on the ground. In another moment
a knee compressed his diaphragm, and a couple of
eager hands gripped his throat, but the grip of one was
weaker than the other; he grasped the wrists, heard a cry
of pain from his assailant, and then the spade of the
navvy came whirling through the air above him, and
struck something with a dull thud. He felt a drop of

 3 **vociferation:** Geschrei.
 7 **to slash:** um sich schlagen.
 8 **conductor:** Schaffner.
19 **counter:** Konter, Gegenschlag.
22 **to compress:** zusammenpressen, eindrücken.
25 **assailant:** Angreifer.

moisture on his face. The grip at his throat suddenly relaxed, and with a convulsive effort Kemp loosed himself, grasped a limp shoulder, and rolled uppermost. He gripped the unseen elbows near the ground. "I've got
5 him!" screamed Kemp. "Help! Help hold! He's down! Hold his feet!"

In another second there was a simultaneous rush upon the struggle, and a stranger coming into the road suddenly might have thought an exceptionally savage game
10 of Rugby football was in progress. And there was no shouting after Kemp's cry, – only a sound of blows and feet and a heavy breathing.

Then came a mighty effort, and the Invisible Man threw off a couple of his antagonists and rose to his knees.
15 Kemp clung to him in front like a hound to a stag, and a dozen hands gripped, clutched, and tore at the Unseen. The tram conductor suddenly got the neck and shoulders and lugged him back.

Down went the heap of struggling men again and rolled
20 over. There was, I am afraid, some savage kicking. Then suddenly a wild scream of "Mercy! Mercy!" that died down swiftly to a sound like choking.

"Get back, you fools!" cried the muffled voice of Kemp, and there was a vigorous shoving back of stalwart forms.
25 "He's hurt, I tell you. Stand back!"

There was a brief struggle to clear a space, and then the circle of eager eyes saw the doctor kneeling, as it seemed, fifteen inches in the air, and holding invisible arms to the ground. Behind him a constable gripped in-
30 visible ankles.

---

15 **stag:** Hirsch.
24 **stalwart:** kräftig, stämmig.

"Don't you leave go of en," cried the big navvy, holding a blood-stained spade; "he's shamming."

"He's not shamming," said the doctor, cautiously raising his knee; "and I'll hold him." His face was bruised and already going red; he spoke thickly because of a bleeding lip. He released one hand and seemed to be feeling at the face. "The mouth's all wet," he said. And then, "Good God!"

He stood up abruptly and then knelt down on the ground by the side of the thing unseen. There was a pushing and shuffling, a sound of heavy feet as fresh people turned up to increase the pressure of the crowd. People now were coming out of the houses. The doors of the Jolly Cricketers were suddenly wide open. Very little was said.

Kemp felt about, his hand seeming to pass through empty air. "He's not breathing," he said, and then, "I can't feel his heart. His side – ugh!"

Suddenly an old woman, peering under the arm of the big navvy, screamed sharply. "Looky there!" she said, and thrust out a wrinkled finger.

And looking where she pointed, everyone saw, faint and transparent as though it was made of glass, so that veins and arteries and bones and nerves could be distinguished, the outline of a hand, a hand limp and prone. It grew clouded and opaque even as they stared.

"Hullo!" cried the constable. "Here's his feet a-showing!"

And so, slowly, beginning at his hands and feet and

---

2 **to sham:** sich verstellen, simulieren.
25 **prone:** am Boden liegend.
26 **to grow clouded:** sich verdichten.

creeping along his limbs to the vital centres of his body, that strange change continued. It was like the slow spreading of a poison. First came the little white nerves, a hazy grey sketch of a limb, then the glassy bones and intricate arteries, then the flesh and skin, first a faint fogginess and then growing rapidly dense and opaque. Presently they could see his crushed chest and his shoulders, and the dim outline of his drawn and battered features.

When at last the crowd made way for Kemp to stand erect, there lay, naked and pitiful on the ground, the bruised and broken body of a young man about thirty. His hair and beard were white, – not grey with age but white with the whiteness of albinism, and his eyes were like garnets. His hands were clenched, his eyes wide open, and his expression was one of anger and dismay.

"Cover his face!" said a man. "For Gawd's sake, cover that face!" and three little children, pushing forward through the crowd, were suddenly twisted round and sent packing off again.

Someone brought a sheet from the Jolly Cricketers; and having covered him, they carried him into that house.

---

1 **vital centres:** Lebenszentren.
4 **hazy:** verschwommen, unscharf.
9 **battered:** zerschlagen, zerschunden.
14 **albinism:** Albinismus, ererbte Unfähigkeit des Körpers, Farbstoffe in Haut, Haaren und Augen zu bilden.
15 **garnet:** Granat (stark glänzendes, braunrotes Mineral, das als Schmuckstein verwendet wird).
21 **to send s.o. packing off** (infml.): jdn. wegschicken.

The Epilogue

So ends the story of the strange and evil experiment of
the Invisible Man. And if you would learn more of him
you must go to a little inn near Port Stowe and talk to the
landlord. The sign of the inn is an empty board save for
a hat and boots, and the name is the title of this story.
The landlord is a short and corpulent little man with a
nose of cylindrical protrusion, wiry hair, and a sporadic
rosiness of visage. Drink generously, and he will tell you
generously of all the things that happened to him after
that time, and of how the lawyers tried to do him out of
the treasure found upon him.

"When they found they couldn't prove who's money was
which, I'm blessed," he says, "if they didn't try to make
me out a blooming treasure trove! Do I *look* like a
Treasure Trove? And then a gentleman gave me a
guinea a night to tell the story at the Empire Music 'all –
just tell 'em in my own words – barring one."

And if you want to cut off the flow of his reminiscences
abruptly, you can always do so by asking if there weren't
three manuscript books in the story. He admits there
were and proceeds to explain, with asseverations that
everybody thinks *he* has 'em! But bless you! he hasn't.

---

1 **epilogue:** Epilog, Nachspiel, Schlußrede.
11 f. **to do s.o. out of s.th.:** jdn. um etwas bringen, erleichtern.
14 f. **to make s.o. out:** jdn. (als etwas) hinstellen.
15 **treasure trove:** Schatz(fund).
17 **guinea:** frühere englische Währungseinheit im Wert von 21 Shilling.
18 **barring one:** bis auf eines, mit einer Ausnahme.
19 **reminiscence:** Erinnerung.
22 **asseveration** (fml.): Beteuerung.

"The Invisible Man it was took 'em off to hide 'em when
I cut and ran for Port Stowe. It's that Mr. Kemp put people on with the idea of *my* having 'em."

And then he subsides into a pensive state, watches you
5 furtively, bustles nervously with glasses, and presently
leaves the bar.

He is a bachelor man – his tastes were ever bachelor, and
there are no women folk in the house. Outwardly he buttons – it is expected of him – but in his more vital priva-
10 cies, in the matter of braces for example, he still turns to
string. He conducts his house without enterprise, but
with eminent decorum. His movements are slow, and he
is a great thinker. But he has a reputation for wisdom
and for a respectable parsimony in the village, and his
15 knowledge of the roads of the South of England would
beat Cobbett.

And on Sunday mornings, every Sunday morning all the
year round, while he is closed to the outer world, and
every night after ten, he goes into his bar parlour bear-

---

1 **the Invisible Man it was took 'em off:** *it was the Invisible Man who
took them off.*
4 **to subside:** (fig.) versinken.
  pensive: nachdenklich.
5 **to bustle with s.th.:** sich an etwas zu schaffen machen.
8f. **to button:** Knöpfe tragen.
9f. **in his more vital privacies** (iron.): in seinen intimeren Privatbereichen.
11 **to conduct:** führen, betreiben.
  enterprise: Unternehmungsgeist.
12 **with eminent decorum:** mit außerordentlichem Anstand.
14 **parsimony:** Knickerigkeit, Geiz.
16 **Cobbett:** William C. (1763–1835), populärer englischer Journalist,
  der eine wichtige Rolle als Fürsprecher des traditionell-ländlichen
  Englands spielte. Hier wird auf seine genauen Kenntnisse der Landschaft des südlichen Englands angespielt.

ing a glass of gin faintly tinged with water; and having placed this down, he locks the door and examines the blinds, and even looks under the table. And then, being satisfied of his solitude, he unlocks the cupboard and a box in the cupboard and a drawer in that box, and produces three volumes bound in brown leather, and places them solemnly in the middle of the table. The covers are weather-worn and tinged with an algal green – for once they sojourned in a ditch and some of the pages have been washed blank by dirty water. The landlord sits down in an armchair, fills a long clay pipe slowly – gloating over the books the while. Then he pulls one towards him and opens it, and begins to study it – turning over the leaves backwards and forwards.

His brows are knit and his lips move painfully. "Hex, little two up in the air, cross and a fiddle-de-dee. Lord! what a one he was for intellect!"

Presently he relaxes and leans back, and blinks through his smoke across the room at things invisible to other eyes. "Full of secrets," he says. "Wonderful secrets! Once I get the haul of them – *Lord!*

I wouldn't do what *he* did; I'd just – well!" He pulls at his pipe.

---

1 **tinged:** leicht getönt, gefärbt.
7 **solemnly** (adv.): feierlich.
8 **algal green:** Algengrün.
9 **to sojourn:** sich aufhalten, verweilen.
11 f. **to gloat over s.th.:** sich an etwas weiden, etwas gierig betrachten.
15 **to knit one's brows:** die Brauen zusammenziehen, die Stirn runzeln.
   hex: verflixt!
16 **fiddle-de-dee:** Schnickschnack.
18 **to blink:** blinzeln.
21 **to get the haul of s.th.:** (fig.) einer Sache auf den Grund kommen, hinter etwas kommen.

So he lapses into a dream, the undying wonderful dream
of his life. And though Kemp has fished unceasingly, and
Adye has questioned closely, no human being save the
landlord knows those books are there, with the subtle
5 secret of invisibility and a dozen other strange secrets
written therein. And none other will know of them until
he dies.

---

2 **to fish** (fig.): suchen, forschen.
   unceasingly (adv.): unablässig, ständig.

Editorische Notiz

Der englische Text folgt der Ausgabe: H. G. Wells, *The Works*, Bd. 3: *The Invisible Man. The War of the Worlds. A Dream of Armageddon*, London: Unwin, 1924 (Atlantic Edition). Das Glossar erklärt in der Regel alle Wörter, die über die Wertigkeitsstufe 4 des *Englischen Arbeitswörterbuches* von Alfred Haase (Frankfurt a. M.: Moritz Diesterweg, ⁷1979) hinausgehen. Im Zweifelsfall wurde großzügig verfahren, d. h. eher eine Vokabel mehr aufgenommen als dort vorgesehen.

Im Glossar verwendete Abkürzungen

adv.	adverb
arch.	archaic (veraltet)
BE	British English
dial.	dialect
fig.	figuratively (übertragen)
fml.	formal (förmlich)
Fr./frz.	French/französisch
infml.	informal (umgangssprachlich)
iron.	ironical
Ital.	Italian
Lat./lat.	Latin/lateinisch
o. s.	oneself
pej.	pejorative (abwertend)
pl.	plural
poet.	poetical (dichterisch, gehoben)
s. o.	someone
s. th.	something
vulg.	vulgar (vulgär, derb)

Literaturhinweise

Aldiss, Brian, *Der Millionen-Jahre-Traum*, Bergisch Gladbach 1980.

Alpers, Hans Joachim / Fuchs, Werner / Hahn, Ronald M. (Hrsg.), *Reclams Science-Fiction-Führer*, Stuttgart 1982.

–/–/–/Jeschke, Wolfgang, *Lexikon der Science-Fiction-Literatur*, München 1988.

Bachelor, J., *H. G. Wells*, Cambridge 1985.

Belgion, Montgomery, *H. G. Wells*, London 1953.

Bergonzi, Bernard, *The Early H. G. Wells. A Study of the Scientific Romances*, Manchester 1961.

– (Hrsg.), *H. G. Wells*, Englewood Cliffs 1976.

Borrello, Alfred, *H. G. Wells. Author in Agony*, Carbondale / Edwardsville (Ill.) 1972.

Braybrooke, Patrick, *Some Aspects of H. G. Wells*, London 1928.

Brome, Vincent, *H. G. Wells. A Biography*, London 1951.

Brooks, Van Wyck, *The World of H. G. Wells*, London 1915.

Brown, Ivor, *H. G. Wells*, London 1923.

Chaplin, F. K., *H. G. Wells: An Outline*, London 1961.

Connes, George, *Études sur la pensée de Wells*, Paris 1926.

Costa, Richard H., *H. G. Wells*, New York 1967.

Dark, Sydney, *The Outline of Wells*, London 1922.

Dickson, Lovat, *H. G. Wells. His Turbulent Life and Times*, Harmondsworth 1972.

Fricker, Robert, *Der moderne englische Roman*, Göttingen ²1966.

Gattégno, Jean, *La science-fiction*, Paris 1973.

Gerber, Richard, *Utopian Fantasy – A Study of English Utopian Fiction since the End of the Nineteenth Century*, London 1955.

Gerhardt, W., *Der Fortschrittsgedanke in den erzählenden Werken von H. G. Wells*, Köln 1955.

Giesen, Rolf, *Lexikon des phantastischen Films*, 2 Bde., Frankfurt a. M. / Berlin / Wien 1984.

Hammond, J. R., *Herbert George Wells*, New York 1977.

Hardt, M. A., *Die Anthropologie H. G. Wells: Darstellung und Kritik eines utopischen Menschenbildes*, Bonn 1948.

Hienger, Jörg, *Literarische Zukunftsphantastik. Eine Studie über Science Fiction*, Göttingen 1972.

Hillegas, Mark R., *The Future as Nightmare: H. G. Wells and the Anti-Utopians*, New York 1967.

Hopkins, R. T., *H. G. Wells: Personality, Character, Topography*, London 1922.

Jansing, H., *Die Darstellung und Konzeption von Naturwissenschaft und Technik in H. G. Wells' »scientific romances«*, Frankfurt a. M. / Bern 1977.

Kagarlitski, Julius, *The Life and Thought of H. G. Wells*, London 1966.

Keenan, Rendall H., *The Major Works of H. G. Wells*, New York 1970.

Lang, Hans-Joachim, *H. G. Wells*, Hamburg 1948.

Lodge, David, *The Novelist at the Crossroads and Other Essays on Fiction and Criticism*, London 1971.

McConnel, Frank, *The Science Fiction of H. G. Wells*, Oxford / New York 1981.

Mackenzie, Norman / Mackenzie, Jeanne, *The Time Traveller*, London 1950.

Nicholls, Peter (Hrsg.), *The Encyclopedia of Science Fiction*, London 1981.

Nicholson, Norman, *H. G. Wells*, London 1950.

Parrinder, Patrick, *H. G. Wells*, New York 1977.

– (Hrsg.), *H. G. Wells: The Critical Heritage*, London 1972.

Philmus, Robert M. / Hughes, David Y. (Hrsg.), *Early Writings in Science and Science Fiction by H. G. Wells*, Berkeley 1975.

Raknem, Ingvald, *H. G. Wells and His Critics*, Oslo 1962.

Roppen, G., "Two Evolutionary Utopias – Homo Sapiens in a Modern Utopia", in: R. G., *Evolution and Poetic Belief*, Oslo 1956, S. 402–466.

Rottensteiner, Franz, *The Science Fiction Book. An Illustrated History*, London 1975.

Scholes, Robert/Rabkin, Eric S., *Science Fiction: History – Science – Vision*, London/Oxford/New York 1977.

Seeßlen, Georg/Kling, Bernt, *Unterhaltung. Lexikon zur populären Kultur*, Bd. 1, Hamburg 1977.

Seeßlen, Georg, *Kino des Utopischen. Geschichte und Mythologie des Science Fiction-Films*, Reinbek b. Hamburg 1980.

Sherman, S. P., "The Utopian Naturalism of H. G. Wells", in: S. S. P., *On Contemporary Literature*, New York [2]1931, S. 50–84.

Sonnemann, U., *Der soziale Gedanke im Werke von H. G. Wells*, Berlin 1935.

Suerbaum, Ulrich/Broich, Ulrich/Borgmeier, Raimund, *Science Fiction. Theorie und Geschichte, Themen und Typen, Form und Weltbild*, Stuttgart 1981.

Suvin, Darko, *Poetik der Science Fiction. Zur Theorie und Geschichte einer literarischen Gattung*, Frankfurt a. M. 1979.

Vallentin, Antonina, *H. G. Wells: Prophet of Our Day*, übers. von Daphne Woodward, New York 1950.

Vernier, Jean-Pierre, *H. G. Wells et son temps*, Rouen 1971.

Wagar, Warren, *H. G. Wells and the World State*, New Haven 1961.

West, Geoffrey, *H. G. Wells: A Sketch for a Portrait*, London 1930.

Williamson, Jack, *H. G. Wells: Critic and Progress*, Baltimore 1973.

Nachwort

Leben und Werk Herbert George Wells'

Herbert George Wells wird am 21. 9. 1866 in Bromley (Kent) als Sohn von Joseph Wells und dessen Frau Sarah geboren. Der Vater betreibt ein wenig gut gehendes Haushaltswarengeschäft, die Mutter arbeitet als Hausangestellte. Im Alter von vierzehn Jahren beginnt Herbert George eine Tuchhändlerlehre, die er zwei Jahre später abbricht. 1883 besucht er die Midhurst Grammar School. Nachdem ihm dort eine Stelle als Hilfslehrer angeboten worden ist, erhält er 1884 ein Stipendium an der Normal School of Science in South Kensington. Er studiert Biologie bei Thomas Henry Huxley, dem berühmten Verfechter der evolutionären Ideen Darwins, der einen starken Einfluß auf ihn ausübt. Wells gerät in finanzielle Schwierigkeiten, betätigt sich politisch und sozial aktiv, wird Sozialist und verliebt sich in seine Kusine Isabel. Die Folge dieser Verwirrungen ist, daß er in seinem Schlußexamen scheitert. Als externer Student erhält er jedoch 1888 den Grad eines Bachelor of Science mit Auszeichnung an der Universität London.

Nach seiner Heirat mit Isabel im Jahre 1891 schlägt sich H. G. Wells als Lehrer, Journalist und Verfasser wissenschaftlicher Lehrbücher durch. Erst 1893 hat er Erfolg als Schriftsteller und wird zum gefragten Autor, Essayisten und Kritiker. Seine frühen Kurzgeschichten erscheinen 1895 unter dem Titel *The Stolen Bacillus and Other Incidents*. Im gleichen Jahr veröffentlicht er seinen ersten Roman, *The Time Machine*. Dieses Werk basiert auf dem 1888 in dem Magazin *Science Schools Journal* erschienenen Fragment *The Chronic Argonauts* und wird zum augenblicklichen Erfolg. Bevor das Jahr 1895 beendet ist, bringt H. G. Wells einen weiteren phantastischen Roman – *The Wonderful Visit* – heraus (darin steigt ein Engel vom Himmel herab und wirft ein kritisches Auge auf die viktorianische Ge-

sellschaft). Bis zum Ende des Jahrhunderts dominieren die
»scientific romances« die literarische Produktion Wells'. Es erscheinen 1896 *The Island of Dr. Moreau* (Thema des »mad
scientist« und der Tiermenschen), 1897 *The Invisible Man* und
The Plattner Story and Others, 1898 *The War of the Worlds* (Invasion vom Mars), 1899 *When the Sleeper Awakes* (der Held er-
wacht in einer totalitären Welt der Zukunft) und *Tales of Space
and Time*. Auch in den Anfangsjahren dieses Jahrhunderts
schreibt H. G. Wells brillante Science Fiction: 1901 *The First
Men in the Moon* (Mondfahrt, intelligente Insektenwesen) und
Twelve Stories and a Dream, 1904 *The Food of the Gods* (Rie-
senwuchs von Pflanzen, Tieren und Kindern), 1906 *In the Day
of the Comet* (ein Komet verändert das Verhalten der Menschen), 1911 *The Country of the Blind and Other Stories* und
The War in the Air (Luftkrieg, Zerstörung durch Bombenan-
griffe), 1913 *The World Set Free: A Story of Mankind* (atomare
Zerstörung in der Zukunft). In seinen utopischen Romanen *A
Modern Utopia* (1905) und *Men Like Gods* (1923) beschreibt
Wells technologisch entwickelte und von einem elitären Sozialismus regierte Gesellschaftsmodelle. In der Novelle *The Shape
of Things to Come* (1933) entwirft er ein Szenario der Zukunft
und zeichnet das Bild einer puritanischen Eliteherrschaft.

Wells' »scientific romances« und utopische Romane, auf die
sich im wesentlichen sein literarischer Ruhm gründen sollte,
spiegeln deutlich ein sozialkritisches und sozialistisches Anliegen wider. 1903 tritt er der Fabian Society bei, die er fünf
Jahre später wieder verläßt, weil er sich mit deren Doktrin von
der nur allmählichen Etablierung des Sozialismus nicht be-
freunden kann. Wells glaubt an die Herausbildung einer intel-
lektuellen Elite – er nennt sie Samurai –, die sich mit Hilfe von
Wissenschaft und Technik der Herausformung eines in eine
ideale Weltordnung einmündenden Gemeinwesens (Weltstaat)
widmet.

Neben Science Fiction und Utopien läßt sich ein zweiter Strang
in Wells' erzählerischem Werk erkennen: die frühen realisti-
schen, autobiographisch geprägten, in Humor und Charakter-
zeichnung an Dickens gemahnenden Gesellschaftsromane. Zu

diesen gehören *The Wheels of Chance* (1896), *Love and Mr. Lewisham* (1900), *Kipps* (1905), *Tono-Bungay, Ann Veronica* (1909), *The History of Mr. Polly* (1910).

Ab 1911, mit dem Erscheinen von *The New Machiavelli*, tendiert H. G. Wells immer stärker zu einer dritten Kategorie seines erzählerischen Werkes: dem Diskussions- oder Ideenroman. Zu ihr gehören *Marriage* (1912), *Mr. Brittling Sees it Through* (1916), *God the Invisible King* (1917), *The World of William Clissold* (3 Bde., 1926).

Nach dem Ersten Weltkrieg wird Wells ein glühender Anhänger des Völkerbundes, muß aber bald enttäuscht dessen Machtlosigkeit einsehen. Es zeigt sich bei ihm eine zunehmende Ungeduld mit den Mitmenschen, die sich in bitterer Kritik in Werken wie *The Undying Fire* (1919) oder *Mr. Blettsworthy on Rampole Island* (1928) entlädt. In den späten dreißiger Jahren wird H. G. Wells Mitglied des Sankey Committee für Menschenrechte, dessen Arbeit die Menschenrechtserklärung der UN-Charta vorwegnimmt. Wells, dem stets die Zukunft der Menschheit als Gesamtheit, Fragen der Erziehung und die Sammlung menschlichen Wissens am Herzen liegen, wendet sich dem Verfassen gewaltiger enzyklopädischer Werke, in denen er das historische, biologische und wirtschaftliche Wissen zusammenträgt, zu: *The Outline of History* (1920), *The Science of Life* (1930, in Zusammenarbeit mit seinem Sohn G. P. Wells und Julian Huxley), *The Work, Wealth and Happiness of Mankind* (1932).

Als einflußreicher Denker wird H. G. Wells auch in Fragen der Weltpolitik immer mehr zu einer festen Größe, was seine Besuche zunächst bei Lenin (1920), dann bei Stalin und Roosevelt (1934) belegen. 1934 faßt er sein Leben und Denken in seinem *Experiment in Autobiography* zusammen. Im gleichen Jahr wird er internationaler Präsident des PEN-Clubs. In seinen späteren Jahren neigt Wells zunehmend zu Pessimismus, was die Zukunft der Menschheit betrifft. *The Fate of Homo Sapiens* (1939) ist von diesem Geist geprägt. In seinem letzten Werk, dem Essay *Mind at the End of its Tether* (1945), entwirft er die düstere Aussicht, daß der Mensch dem Untergang geweiht ist,

weil er sich den technologischen Bedingungen weder anpassen
will noch kann. Der Zweite Weltkrieg, an dessen Ende dieses
Werk entstanden ist, hat Wells, der die Katastrophe vorausge-
sagt hat, zutiefst deprimiert und den zeitlebens bei ihm vorhan-
denen pessimistischen Grundzug deutlich verstärkt. Am 13.
August 1956 stirbt H. G. Wells beinahe achtzigjährig in Lon-
don.
Mit über hundertfünfzig Büchern, Pamphleten, Hörspielen und
Drehbüchern ist der Engländer einer der produktivsten
Schriftsteller aller Zeiten.

II

»The Invisible Man«

Der Einbruch des Grauenhaften

Bereits das erste Kapitel der grotesken Romanze *The Invisible
Man* enthält eine Reihe struktureller und situativer Züge, die
sie mit der phantastischen bzw. Schreckensliteratur teilt. Wie so
oft in den phantastischen Romanen und Kurzgeschichten
Wells' (z. B. in *The War of the Worlds*) erfolgt der Einbruch des
Phantastischen, Geheimnisvollen, Unerklärlichen inmitten der
alltäglichen Umgebung der südenglischen Landschaft. Als
Grundsituation findet sich ein phantastisches Element, das die
Behaglichkeit der viktorianischen Umwelt aus den Fugen
reißt.[1] Durch das Einbetten des Geschehens in ein kleinbürger-
lich-ländliches Milieu – Schauplatz ist der kleine Ort Iping in
Sussex – wird das Mysteriöse nicht nur ins Grauenhafte gestei-
gert, sondern gleichzeitig glaubwürdig gemacht.
Bereits der erste Satz des Eingangskapitels evoziert das Element des Fremden bzw. der Befremdlichkeit im Auftreten ei-
nes namenlosen Unbekannten. Bezeichnenderweise taucht der
Fremde nicht an einem lichterfüllten und farbenprächtigen
Frühlings-, Sommer- oder Herbsttag auf, sondern bei beißen-

---

1 Siehe Darko Suvin, »H. G. Wells als Angelpunkt der SF-Tradition«, in:
   D. S., *Poetik der Science Fiction,* Frankfurt a. M. 1979, S. 265.

dem Winterwetter. Auch dieser atmosphärische Eingangsrahmen ist ein Strukturmittel, das sich in der phantastischen Literatur nicht selten findet: Schnee bzw. Schneesturm als atmosphärische Begleiterscheinung grauenhafter und angsteinflößender Ereignisse. Man denke an den Blizzard in Stephen Kings Erzählung *One for the Road* oder den alles zudeckenden Schnee in Truman Capotes phantastischer Novelle *Miriam*. In beiden Geschichten tauchen wie bei Wells gleichsam aus dem Nichts Fremde auf, die Befremden und Angst erzeugen. Ist die äußere Erscheinung des Fremden – seine totale Vermummung – von den Widrigkeiten des Winterwetters her gesehen plausibel, so mutet sein Hineinwanken in das am idyllischen Namen »The Coach and Horses« tragende Gasthaus »more dead than alive« und seine melodramatischen Worte »A fire [...] in the name of human charity« recht befremdlich an. Vollends befremdlich wirkt das Verhalten des Fremden auf Mrs. Hall, die Wirtin, als er in dem inzwischen von einem Feuer erwärmten Salon, den er in Beschlag nimmt, zunächst keine Anstalten macht, Hut, Mantel und Handschuhe abzulegen. Der Umschlag des nur Seltsam-Befremdlichen ins Grauenhafte findet in dem Moment statt, als Mrs. Hall das Gesicht des Fremden, nachdem er Hut und Mantel abgelegt hat, wahrnimmt. Hier baut der Autor ein beträchtliches Potential an Spannung und Verrätselung auf, das nicht zuletzt von der Beschreibung der von Überraschung, Schock und Angst geprägten Reaktion Mrs. Halls auf die überaus seltsame Erscheinung des Fremden getragen wird. Dieser verhüllt nämlich Mund und Kinn mit einem weißen Tuch, woraus seine nuschelnde Aussprache resultiert; der übrige Teil des Kopfes ist völlig zubandagiert, lediglich eine blaugetönte, undurchsichtige Brille sowie eine glänzende rosa Nasenspitze sind sichtbar. Die vom Autor aufgebaute Spannung ist nun derart intensiv, daß der Leser sich angesichts des Fremden fragen muß, welche Bewandtnis es mit dessen seltsamer Vermummung hat. Nicht nur die äußere Aufmachung, sondern auch Verhalten und Redeweise – die kurz angebundene, ja aggressive, der Wirtin über den Mund fahrende Diktion – bieten Anlaß zu Spekulation. Im übrigen bildet diese Redeweise einen deutlichen Kontrast zu dem südwestenglischen, von Aussprachebesonderheiten (wie z. B. »aitch-dropping«), agrammatischen Solezismen (»them bandages«, »they goggles«) und Fehlern (»opration«) durchsetzten Regiolekt Mrs. Halls und bildet Teil des Gegensatzes von Grauen und Alltäglichkeit. Bevor der Leser seinen Schluß ziehen bzw. seine Vermutungen anstellen kann, läßt Wells die Wirtin ihre eigenen Spekulationen über die seltsame Aufmachung des Fremden anstellen: ein Unfall oder eine Operation habe diesen entstellt, so daß er sein Gesicht verbergen müsse. Diese Vermutung wird in der Tat durch den Fremden selbst bestätigt, als er (Kap. 2) einen ersten Hinweis auf seine Identität gibt – »I am an experimental investigator« – und in diesem Zusammenhang von einem Mißgeschick (»accident«) spricht, das ihm widerfahren sei und ihm eine zurückgezogene Lebensweise aufzwinge. Mit diesen Fingerzeigen einschließlich dem Hinweis auf Geräte und Apparate, die der Fremde mit sich führt, und auf ein Blatt mit mathematischen Formeln, das er im Salon hinterläßt, hat sich das um den seltsamen Besucher aufgebaute Rätsel- und Spannungspotential derart verstärkt, daß es nach Auflösung drängt. Was der Spannung eine besondere, der phantastischen Literatur spezifische Dimension verleiht, ist deren Verknüpfung mit der Stimmung des Unheimlichen und Grotesken, die sich bereits in der Wortwahl ausdrückt. Der Fremde, in den Augen Mrs. Halls »an unusually strange sort of stranger«, erscheint dem Uhrmacher Teddy Henfrey »grotesque« und »uncanny-looking«. An anderer Stelle (Kap. 4) ist von dem »skull-like head«, dem »ghastly bandaged face« und der befremdlichen Tatsache die Rede, daß der Fremde Kindern, die seiner ansichtig werden, Träume vom schwarzen Mann (»bogies«) einjage. Und wenn die Wirtin dem grotesken Gast mitteilt, jemand werde kommen, um die alte Uhr im Salon zu richten, herrscht in dem verdunkelten, von der roten Glut des Kaminfeuers nur schwach erleuchteten Raum eine unheimliche Atmosphäre, die durch die Erscheinung des seltsamen Fremden ins Schreckliche gesteigert wird. Voller Schock starrt Mrs. Hall auf den bandagierten Kopf, die monströsen (»monstrous«) Brillengläser und

den enormen, weit offenen Mund, der die untere Hälfte des
Gesichts zu verschlingen scheint. Mit einer derart grotesk-un-
heimlichen Darstellung des Fremden fordert Wells geradezu
den Vergleich mit einem »bug-eyed monster« heraus, wie wir es
aus den »pulp magazines« der zwanziger und dreißiger Jahre
oder den amerikanischen SF-B-movies der fünfziger Jahre ken-
nen.[2] Auch der Mann der Wirtin erlebt den Fremden umgeben
von einer Aura des Geheimnisvollen, Grauenhaften und Unheimlichen, wenn er dessen Arm ohne Hand sieht (»a handless
arm waving towards him«). Als später Mrs. Hall das Zimmer
des Fremden erneut betritt und sieht, daß dieser seine Brille abgelegt hat, kommen ihr seine Augenhöhlen ungewöhnlich tief
vor. All dies verwirrt sie ebenso wie die zahlreichen Flaschen
und Reagenzgläser, die der Fremde auf sein Zimmer bringen
läßt. Verwirrend sind auch die hinter der verschlossenen Tür zu
hörenden merkwürdigen Geräusche – das Klirren von Glas, das
Zerbersten einer Flasche, hastige Schritte, verzweifelte Ausrufe.

Bei der Evozierung des Grauen- und Geheimnisvollen greift
Wells allerdings auch auf jenes strukturelle Mittel zurück, das
die aufgebaute Spannung deutlich auflockert: den *comic relief.*
Ist durch die dialektal-ländliche Ausdrucksweise der Dorfbe-
wohner bereits ein erheiternder Kontrapunkt gegeben, so wirkt
ein Ereignis wie der sich auf den Fremden stürzende Hund, der
mit den Zähnen dessen Handschuh und Hosenbein zerreißt,
einschließlich der absurd-einfältigen Spekulation Fearensides,
des Hundebesitzers – aus den Rissen in des Fremden Kleidung
schließt er, daß dieser zumindest teilweise von schwarzer Haut-
farbe sei (Kap. 3) –, keineswegs unheimlich, sondern eher be-
lustigend. Überhaupt erscheint der Fremde in dieser Szene
eher komisch als schrecklich. Erheiternd ist auch das Entsetzen, das der Landarzt Cuss verspürt, als er, von Neugier getrie-
ben, sich in das Zimmer des Fremden wagt und von dessen unsichtbaren Fingern in die Nase gezwickt wird (Kap. 4). Man

---

2 H. G. Wells lieferte in der Tat das Modell für die »bug-eyed monsters«
der späteren Science Fiction.

kann B. Bergonzi zustimmen, wenn er bezüglich der ersten Kapitel von *The Invisible Man* feststellt, diese enthielten »some of Wells' finest social comedy«[3].

Durch das Mittel des *comic relief* wird – wie gesagt – die Spannung aufgelockert, sie läßt jedoch keineswegs nach. Im Gegenteil, wie letzterer Vorfall zeigt, steigt sie durch die Frage, wie es sich mit einem Mann verhält, an dessen Arm keine Hand zu sehen ist, der aber dennoch – wie Cuss deutlich fühlen konnte – über Hand und Finger verfügt, wiederum stark an. Der Gedanke, daß dem Fremden irgendeine Art von Mißgeschick widerfahren ist, wird von diesem selbst erneut aufgegriffen. Er, der Experimentator, gibt Cuss in wenigen Worten zu verstehen, daß bei seinen Experimenten irgend etwas schiefgelaufen ist, was ein Licht auf sein gequältes und reizbares Wesen wirft. Ein für ihn wichtiges Rezept sei von einem Windstoß in den Kamin geweht worden und verbrannt. Wells, der mit dem Hundebiß und dem Arm ohne Hand bereits wichtige Indizien hinsichtlich des rätselhaften Zustands des Fremden eingestreut hat, gibt in Kapitel 5 einen besonders deutlichen Hinweis, der die Erzählung ein weiteres Stück näher an die Enthüllung dessen bringt, was es mit dem Fremden auf sich hat. Der dort geschilderte Einbruch ins Pfarrhaus zeigt einen Einbrecher, der völlig unsichtbar ist; man sieht ihn nicht, aber man hört ihn und sieht die Spuren seines Wirkens. Eines der Geräusche, das er verursacht, ist ein Niesen, das auf eine Erkältung schließen läßt. Eine Erkältung hat auch Cuss im vorherigen Kapitel bei dem Fremden festgestellt. Es liegt somit der Schluß nah, daß der Fremde der unsichtbare Einbrecher ist, der in das Pfarrhaus einbricht, um seine knappen finanziellen Ressourcen aufzufrischen. In dieser Episode erweist sich Wells wiederum als Meister der Evozierung einer unheimlichen, mysteriösen und spannungsgeladenen Atmosphäre. Ganz in der Tradition des Schauergenres wurzelnd, greift er auf das für die Gothic novel typische Requisit des »haunted house« zurück, in welchem im Morgen-

---

3 Bernard Bergonzi, *The Early H. G. Wells. A Study of the Scientific Romances,* Manchester 1961, S. 116.

grauen scheinbar unerklärliche Dinge geschehen, rätselhafte
Geräusche zu vernehmen sind, Treppen knarren, eine Tür sich
wie ein Abgrund auftut, ein unsichtbares Wesen – ein Geist? –
sein Unwesen treibt und den geistlichen Herrn nebst seiner Frau (deren Schilderung als »quaintly-costumed little
couple« unverhohlen komisch und augenzwinkernd erfolgt) erschreckt.

Obwohl aufgrund der Ereignisse jedem, selbst dem schwerfäl-
ligen Mr. Hall, klargeworden ist, daß zwischen dem nächtlichen
Einbrecher und dem rätselhaften Fremden ein Zusammenhang
bestehen muß (»two and two were put together«), löst die Enthüllung des letzteren bei den Dorfbewohnern keineswegs einen
Aha-Effekt aus, sondern versetzt sie in Entsetzen und Panik
(Kap. 7).

Die erste Enthüllung des Unsichtbaren

Die Enthüllung des Fremden im Gasthaus sowie die Reaktion
der anwesenden Bürger von Iping darauf vollziehen sich als
groteske Mischung aus Grauen und Komik. Der Fremde, wegen unbezahlter Rechnungen von Mrs. Hall in die Enge getrie-
ben, ist bereit, den in der Bar Anwesenden seinen wahren Zustand wenn nicht zu erklären, so doch vor Augen zu führen. Paradoxerweise enthüllt ihnen das grauenvolle Spektakel gerade
nicht, was sie am ehesten erwarteten – Narben oder Entstel-
lungen bei dem Fremden –, sondern dessen Unsichtbarkeit, die
durch das Ablegen seiner »Maskierung« offenkundig wird. Die
grauenvolle Demaskierung und die Entdeckung der sich bewe-
genden Kleidung ohne Körper lösen bei den Wirtshausbesu-
chern Verwirrung, Ungläubigkeit (»some conjuring trick«), vor
allem aber Schrecken und Panik aus. Das Geständnis des Fremden, daß er sehr wohl über Kopf, Rumpf und Gliedmaßen ver-
füge, aber unsichtbar sei, bedeutet den absoluten Höhepunkt
und zugleich die Auflösung der sorgfältig aufgebauten Spannung, die aus der Frage resultierte, welche Bewandtnis es mit
dem grotesken Mummenschanz des Fremden und dessen be-
fremdlichem Verhalten hat. Freilich baut sich nun ein weiteres

Spannungsfeld aus der Frage nach der Ursache der Unsichtbarkeit auf.

Strukturell ist mit dem Enthüllungskapitel die erste Phase des
Romans abgeschlossen, was durch die Tatsache markiert ist,
daß der namenlose Fremde von dem omniszienten Erzähler –
einem Berichterstatter in der ersten Person – nunmehr als »Invisible Man«, nicht mehr als »stranger« apostrophiert wird.

Mit dem Aufgreifen des Themas der Unsichtbarkeit begibt sich
Wells in die Tradition altgermanischer Sagen (wie z. B. die Ni-
belungensage) und Märchen, deren Tarnkappenmotiv er rezi-
piert. Während die Unsichtbarkeit dort wie auch in jugendli-
chen Tagträumen als Zustand grenzenloser Wunscherfüllung
und Freiheit ungeahnte Möglichkeiten eröffnet, ist sie für den
namenlosen Fremden in Wells' Romanze ein Fluch (»It's a confounded nuisance«). Damit stellt der Autor das Märchenmotiv
auf den Kopf. Zu Recht bezeichnet Darko Suvin *The Invisible
Man* als »invertiertes Märchen«[4]. Als Fluch gestaltet sich die
Unsichtbarkeit, weil sich mit ihr der Fremde außerhalb der Gesellschaft stellt, die ihn ächtet und ausgrenzt. Damit ähnelt er
dem Helden in Robert Silverbergs brillanter dystopischer Erzählung *To See the Invisible Man* (1963), dessen Unsichtbarkeit
als Nicht-Gesehen-Werden-Dürfen durch die Mitmenschen die
Strafe für ein Vergehen ist und zu sozialer Ächtung und damit
unendlicher Einsamkeit führt.

Auch der Unsichtbare bei Wells ist einsam, befindet sich offen-
sichtlich in einer Notlage, fühlt sich bedroht und muß deshalb
seine Unsichtbarkeit hinter Kleidern, Bandage, künstlicher
Nase und falschem Haar verbergen. Das Ganze vollzieht sich
als Paradox: ein Mann erlebt den Fluch der Unsichtbarkeit und
versucht diesen innerhalb der Gesellschaft untragbaren und
unerträglichen Zustand durch den Anschein von Sichtbarkeit
zu verbergen, d. h. seine Unsichtbarkeit unsichtbar für die anderen zu machen.

Die aus diesem Zustand zwangsläufig resultierenden Probleme
führen den Unsichtbaren unweigerlich in die Gesetzlosigkeit.

4 D. Suvin, *Poetik der Science Fiction*, S. 272.

Aufgrund seiner Situation nicht in der Lage, ein Einkommen zu sichern, begeht er Einbruch und Diebstahl, macht Schulden, überfällt ein Mädchen, dem er das Brot stiehlt, wird beleidigend, begeht Körperverletzung. Obwohl diese Vergehen aus seiner Notlage heraus entstehen, lassen sie ihn im Sinne der Justiz schuldig werden und veranlassen die Exekutive, vertreten durch den Dorfpolizisten Bobby Jaffers, ihn zu verhaften. Der Verhaftung entzieht sich der Unsichtbare durch Flucht.

Das der Flucht unmittelbar vorausgehende Kampfgetümmel, dessen komische Seite sich aus dem Charakter einer dörflichen Wirtshausschlägerei und dessen grotesker Zug sich daraus ergibt, daß ein Unsichtbarer direkter Anlaß des Tumults und Kampfgegner der im Gasthaus versammelten Gäste ist, leitet eine neue Phase des Romans ein. Der Unsichtbare verläßt Iping, ein Schauplatzwechsel findet statt. Es bestätigen sich zwei Vermutungen, die die Bewohner von Iping zuvor (Kap. 4) über den Unsichtbaren angestellt haben: er sei ein flüchtiger Krimineller bzw. ein Anarchist. Beide Vermutungen erweisen sich durch den Gang der Ereignisse als richtig. Der Unbekannte ist kriminell geworden und befindet sich auf der Flucht, als Anarchist hat er unerkannt unter den Menschen gelebt und sie in Angst und Schrecken versetzt.[5] Ehe der Unsichtbare gänzlich aus Iping verschwindet, kehrt er allerdings noch einmal dorthin zurück, denn dort hat er seine Habseligkeiten zurücklassen müssen. Mit Hilfe des Landstreichers Marvel – einer Gestalt wie aus einem Roman Dickens' – besorgt er sich Kleidung und holt sich seine unersetzlichen Notizbücher aus dem Salon des Gasthauses. Seine Rückkehr nach Iping bleibt dort allerdings nicht unbemerkt. Auf recht unsanfte Weise veranlaßt er den Landarzt und den Pfarrer – beide müssen sich ihrer Kleidung entledigen und sie an ihn herausrücken –, ihm zu helfen. Erneut sucht der Unsichtbare das Weite, und eine wilde Verfolgungsjagd setzt ein, in deren von zahlreichen komischen Details durchsetzten Verlauf der Fremde seinem Ruf als Chaot

5 Siehe Hans Joachim Alpers / Werner Fuchs / Roland Hahn (Hrsg.), *Reclams Science-Fiction-Führer,* Stuttgart 1982, S. 449.

und Terrorist alle Ehre macht. Brutal und rücksichtslos seine Unsichtbarkeit ausnutzend, verbreitet er Schrecken und Verwirrung. Als er in dem Getümmel selbst einen schmerzhaften Schlag ins Gesicht erhält, gerät er in blinde Raserei. Die Worte des Arztes – »he's gone mad« (Kap. 12) – stellen angesichts der sinnlosen Zerstörungswut, die von dem unsichtbaren Terroristen Besitz ergreift – er zerschlägt Fensterscheiben und durchschneidet den Telegraphendraht –, eine deutliche Untertreibung dar.

Den Ablauf des in eine neue Phase tretenden und mit einem Schauplatzwechsel verknüpften Plots gestaltet H. G. Wells mit den strukturellen Mitteln der Duplizität und Äquivalenz der Ereignisse. In dem Ort Burdock – dem neuen Schauplatz – führt der Weg des Unsichtbaren wiederum in ein Gasthaus namens »The Jolly Cricketers« (Kap. 16). Dorthin folgt er dem Landstreicher Marvel, der ihm zu entkommen trachtet (dieser ist immer noch im Besitz der unersetzlichen Notizbücher). Es entsteht wiederum Panik unter der Bevölkerung. In dem Schreckensruf »The Invisible Man is coming! *The Invisible Man!*« artikuliert sich die Angst vor dem Grauenhaften und Unerklärlichen. Der im folgenden Gasthausgetümmel durch einen Schuß verletzte Unbekannte flüchtet sich in das Haus des Wissenschaftlers Dr. Kemp (Kap. 17). Hier vollzieht sich eine weitere Äquivalenz bzw. eine Verdichtung von Kapitel 7, insofern als eine erneute Enthüllung, diesmal der Identität des Unsichtbaren, vonstatten geht.

Die zweite Enthüllung des Unbekannten

Dem Wissenschaftler Dr. Kemp enthüllt der Unbekannte seinen Namen, schildert ihm sein Aussehen, als er noch sichtbar war, und verweist auf die Tatsache, daß er als begabter Chemiker am Universitäts-College gearbeitet hat. Aus dieser Zeit ist ihm Kemp, in dessen Haus er zufällig geraten ist, bekannt. Wie bei der ersten Enthüllung aus dem Fremden der Unsichtbare wurde, wird nun aus dem Unsichtbaren Griffin – so sein Name. Das Zusammentreffen zweier Wissenschaftler und – wie noch

auszuführen ist – zweier Wissenschaftlertypen zeigt eine völlig
neue Personenkonstellation. War Griffin bisher nur mit – wie er
sich ausdrückt – »bumpkins« oder »yokels« konfrontiert bzw.
mit einem vertrottelten Arzt, einem senilen Pfarrer, einem
wichtigtuerischen Dorfpolizisten oder einem harmlosen Landstreicher, so trifft er nun auf einen Ebenbürtigen, auf dessen
Hilfe er hofft und den er ins Vertrauen zieht.

Auf das völlig überraschende Konfrontiertwerden mit einem
Unsichtbaren in seinem Haus reagiert der Naturwissenschaft-
ler Dr. Kemp zunächst ganz und gar nicht wie ein solcher. Allzu
absurd und grotesk ist das Phänomen, daß er es – zumal die un-
mittelbaren psychologischen Auswirkungen des Ereignisses
ihn besonders belasten – an den Parametern der Naturwissen-
schaften messen könnte. Nachdem Kemp der aus der Wunde
Griffins stammenden geronnenen Blutstropfen gewahr geworden ist, hält er dessen Stimme, die plötzlich aus dem Raum er-
tönt, für eine Sinnestäuschung, und er reagiert mit »superstitious inklings«. Das Gefühl, das ihn befällt, ist das des Unheimlichen (»eerie«). Kemp reagiert so, wie es Sigmund Freud in
seiner Schrift *Das Unheimliche* (1919) dargestellt hat. Die
Denkweise seiner primitiven Vorfahren, die rätselhafte Vorgänge, prompte Wunscherfüllung, Wiederkehr von Toten, geheime schädigende Kräfte oder die Allmacht von Gedanken
für Wirklichkeit hielten, hat der moderne, skeptische Mensch
überwunden. Er glaubt nicht mehr an diese Vorgänge. Allerdings nur so lange, bis sich in seinem Leben etwas ereignet, das
die primitiven Überzeugungen, die nach wie vor in ihm lauern,
zu bestätigen scheint. Es stellt sich bei ihm, in dem der alte
Aberglaube noch unbewußt fortlebt, das Gefühl der Unheimlichkeit ein.[6] Als der von abergläubischer Furcht befallene
Kemp einen blutbefleckten Leinenverband im Raum schweben
sieht und eine Stimme seinen Namen ruft, um ihm mitzuteilen,
sie gehöre einem Unsichtbaren, weicht jedoch das Gefühl des
Unheimlichen erneut der Skepsis des Naturwissenschaftlers: er

6 Vgl. Sigmund Freud, »Das Unheimliche« (1919), in: S. F., *Studienaus-
gabe,* hrsg. von Alexander Mitscherlich, Bd. 4: *Psychologische Schrif-
ten,* Frankfurt a. M. 1970, S. 270.

hält das Ganze für einen ausgemachten Unsinn, für einen Trick (dies eine weitere Duplizität gegenüber der ersten Enthüllungsszene: auch dort glaubte man an einen Zaubertrick). Doch der Schock der körperlichen Berührung fegt die Rationalität des Wissenschaftlers wiederum weg; dieser reagiert instinkthaft, panisch, irrational, und Griffin ermahnt ihn streng: »Listen to reason, will you«. Die Ratio in Form der wissenschaftlichen Erklärung liegt dem sich in emotionalem Schockzustand befindlichen Kemp jedoch fern: für das Schauspiel der Unheimlichkeit mit all seinen grotesken und verwirrenden Begleiterscheinungen – Wells wandelt hier wieder in den Spuren des Schauerromans – kann er nur Worte wie »horrible«, »strange and wonderful«, »insane«, »unreasonable«, »frantic« finden. Sein Verstand sträubt sich, das Faktum der Unsichtbarkeit zu akzeptieren. Er sieht darin das Ergebnis von Hypnose, zweifelt an seinem eigenen Verstand und schließt angesichts dieser »flagrant absurdity« die Möglichkeit eines Traums nicht aus, ja geht sogar so weit, zu vermuten, daß nur Teufelswerk (»devilry«) einen Menschen unsichtbar machen könne. Der Wissenschaftler, unfähig, ein ihm unerklärliches, absurd erscheinendes Phänomen rational zu fassen, flüchtet sich seinerseits in das Absurdum einer abergläubischen Spekulation – mit Freud gesprochen, es bricht der alte Aberglaube, der in ihm lauert, wieder auf.

Die dritte Enthüllung des Unsichtbaren

Erneut hat sich um die Frage nach der Ursache der Unsichtbarkeit Griffins ein Spannungspotential aufgebaut, das so sehr angewachsen ist, daß seine Auflösung zwangsläufig erfolgen muß. Wiederum greift H. G. Wells zu dem Mittel der Enthüllung und leitet die letzte Phase jenes Prozesses ein, der im Lüften des Geheimnisses besteht. Dieses Mal geschieht die Enthüllung in Form eines umfangreichen, insgesamt fünf Kapitel (Kap. 19–23) umfassenden rückblendenden Berichts, den Griffin Dr. Kemp gibt. Dieser Bericht – nur gelegentlich unterbrochen durch kurze Kommentare, Zwischenfragen, erstaunte

Ausrufe und kritische Bemerkungen Kemps (»odd«, »Ah«, »Great Heavens«, »Phew«) – läßt die turbulenten, aber auch schrecklichen Erlebnisse des Unsichtbaren sowie die bizarren Ereignisse, die sich um ihn herum, angefangen von seinen Studententagen bis zur Ankunft in Iping, abgespielt haben, Revue passieren. In nuce enthält diese umfassende Bestandsaufnahme die folgenden Ebenen bzw. Bereiche:

– den (pseudo)wissenschaftlichen Diskurs Griffins über die Entdeckung der Möglichkeit, feste oder flüssige Körper unsichtbar zu machen, sowie das zugrundeliegende naturwissenschaftliche Prinzip (Kap. 19), das Experiment mit der Katze, die eigene Unsichtbarwerdung (Kap. 20);

– Stationen des Lebenswegs und des wissenschaftlichen Werdegangs des Unsichtbaren: Studium der Medizin und Physik, Faszinosum der Gesetze der Optik, Forschung und Lehrtätigkeit, die Vision von der Unsichtbarkeit als Weg zu Macht, Freiheit und ungeahnten Möglichkeiten, der Mangel an Geld, der das geheime Forschungsprojekt zu zerschlagen droht. Daraus resultierend:

– das Geständnis, den Vater bestohlen zu haben, der – da das Geld nicht das seine war – aus Verzweiflung Selbstmord begeht (Kap. 19);

– Griffins moralische Depravation: die Abwesenheit jeglicher Reue gegenüber dem Schicksal des Vaters, der Gefühls- und Gewissensverlust, die cholerische Reizbarkeit, die manische Besessenheit von der fixen Idee, das Experiment an sich selbst durchführen zu müssen, die Gewalt gegen den Besitzer des Hauses, in dem sich Wohnung und Laboratorium Griffins befindet, das skrupellose Niederbrennen des Hauses (Kap. 20);

– ungeahnte Probleme und Kehrseiten der Unsichtbarkeit: schmerzhafte Kollisionen mit Menschen und Fahrzeugen, Nacktheit und Kälte, Gefahren des Entdecktwerdens, Ausgestoßensein und Nichtmenschsein, Maskierung und Verfolgung (Kap. 21–23);

– der weitere moralische Niedergang Griffins, der seinen

Tiefpunkt in Gewalt, Brutalität und im Einbruchsdiebstahl (im Laden in Drury Lane) findet, wobei letzteres auch aus der Not der Verzweiflung des Unsichtbaren resultiert; die der Enttäuschung und Ernüchterung erwachsende Einsicht, »what a helpless absurdity an Invisible Man was« (Kap. 23).

Griffins Bericht endet mit dessen Ankunft in Iping, wo er hofft (siehe Kap. 23), durch Experimente seine Sichtbarkeit wiederzugewinnen. Dazu benötigt er die sich immer noch im Besitz des Landstreichers Marvel befindlichen Notizbücher.

Der »mad scientist«

Wie zu sehen war, finden sich an verschiedenen Stellen des Buches im Zusammenhang mit dem Auftauchen des Unsichtbaren Bezeichnungen für diesen wie »strange« oder »grotesque«, aber auch Appellativa wie »lunatic« (die in Kapitel 4 geäußerte Vermutung, es handle sich bei Griffin um einen harmlosen Verrückten, erweist sich freilich als falsch), »insane« (Kap. 17) und »mad« (Kap. 12 und 18). Innerhalb seines Berichts bezeichnet Griffin selbst sein Experiment als »mad« (Kap. 23). Die Verknüpfung des Begriffes »wahnsinnig« mit wissenschaftlichem Experimentieren bzw. mit dem, der diese Experimente durchführt, deutet auf einen Topos hin, der in Science-Fiction- und Horror-Literatur bzw. -Filmen überaus häufig anzutreffen ist: der des »mad scientist«. Griffin ist der wahnsinnige Wissenschaftler, Ort und Umgebung seines Experimentierens weisen die typischen Züge des den »mad scientist«-Topos umgebenden Ambiente auf. Verrückt ist Griffin in dem Sinne, als er ein von einer fixen Idee besessener Neurotiker ist, dessen einzige Liebe seinen Experimenten gilt und dessen Ziel, die Unsichtbarkeit zu erreichen, er mit allen Mitteln und unter Mißachtung der ethischen Normen des menschlichen Zusammenlebens durchzusetzen sucht. Griffin wird von Wells in die Traditionslinie teuflischer Wissenschaftler eingereiht, die sich von E. T. A. Hoffmann (*Der Sandmann*, 1816), Mary Shelley (*Frankenstein*,

1818), H. de Balzac (*La Recherche de l'absolu*, 1834), bis ins späte 19. Jahrhundert (R. L. Stevenson, *The Strange Case of Dr. Jekyll and Mr. Hyde*, 1886) erstreckt und ihre Fortsetzung in der modernen Horror- und Science-Fiction-Literatur dieses Jahrhunderts einschließlich des Filmgenres findet. In der Gestalt des »mad scientists« kommt es häufig zu einer Allianz des von manischer Sucht nach Übermenschlichkeit getriebenen Gelehrten und des naturwissenschaftlichen Genies. In dieser Figur personifiziert sich die prometheische Auflehnung gegen die göttliche Ordnung und körperliche Begrenzung des Menschen.[7] Nicht selten wird der »mad scientist« als physisch mißgestaltet dargestellt, erscheint mithin nicht nur in ethischer, sondern auch physischer Hinsicht als Außenseiter. Griffins Beschreibung als Albino mit weißer Haut und roten Augen (Kap. 17) entspricht diesem körperlichen Außenseitertum, das ihn seit seiner Geburt von seinen Mitmenschen abhebt, was sein gleichgültiges Verhalten diesen gegenüber psychologisch erklärt. Häufig sind die Schauplätze des wahnhaften Experimentierens in dunklen Gewölben, düsteren Schlössern oder alten, heruntergekommenen Häusern verborgene Laboratorien. So auch in *The Invisible Man*. Griffin hat sich in einem heruntergekommenen Haus, das sich in einem Slumviertel in der Nähe der Great Portland Street befindet, eingemietet, um dort seine Experimente durchzuführen. Diese Ortswahl ist nicht zufällig, ist doch die schmutzige Umgebung mit ihren an Gestalten aus den Romanen Dickens' erinnernden Figuren (Hausbesitzer und Mitbewohner) Spiegelbild der moralischen Depravation des Wissenschaftlers. Ein weiterer struktureller Zug, der nicht selten in »mad scientist«-Geschichten auftaucht, findet auch in Wells' Romanze Eingang: Bevor das zentrale und entscheidende (Selbst-)Experiment stattfindet, nimmt der Wissenschaftler einen Tierversuch vor, der häufig mißlingt.[8] Das Ex-

---

7 Siehe dazu Georg Seeßlen, *Kino des Utopischen*, Reinbek bei Hamburg 1980, S. 116–119, und Peter Nicholls (Hrsg.), The *Encyclopedia of Science Fiction*, London 1979, S. 533.
8 Dieser Zug findet sich z. B. in der bekannten, zweimal verfilmten Horrorgeschichte *The Fly* (1957) von George Langelaan.

periment mit der weißen Katze, das Griffin vornimmt, geht insofern schief, als das Tier zwar unsichtbar wird, seine Augen und Pfoten aber sichtbar bleiben – ein unheimliches Spektakel (»there remained two little ghosts of her eyes«, Kap. 20), das Wells atmosphärisch dicht und spannend-schaurig darzustellen vermag. Das Ganze ist eingebettet in die düstere Atmosphäre des alten Hauses, die an den Schauertopos des »haunted house« erinnert.

Die absolute Besessenheit und monomanische Arbeitswut zerstören nicht nur Griffins moralische Substanz, sondern verlangen auch ihren körperlichen Preis. Apathie und physische Erschöpfung sind die Folge dieses Raubbaus, den der Wissenschaftler durch die Einnahme des drogenartigen Stärkungsmittels Strychnin zu korrigieren sucht. Bemerkenswert ist die Reaktion Kemps, als Griffin ihm von der Einnahme dieser Droge berichtet: er bezeichnet sie als »the devil«, »the palaeolithic in the bottle« (Kap. 20). Was sich in diesen Ausdrücken artikuliert, ist der viktorianische Gedanke von der Abspaltung und Verselbständigung des Bösen – hier bewirkt durch die Einnahme einer Droge –, von der Bestie im Menschen, ein Gedanke, den Wells' Landsmann und Zeitgenosse R. L. Stevenson in seiner Horrorgeschichte von dem schrecklichen Doppelwesen Dr. Jekyll / Mr. Hyde eindringlich thematisiert. (Wie Wells in Kapitel 6 seines *Experiment in Autobiography* berichtet, ist er von Stevenson angeregt worden.) Griffin fühlt sich nach der Einnahme der Droge gestärkt und zugleich reizbar-cholerisch. Das Teuflische, Animalische, Unvernünftige, Zerstörerische, der instinkthaft reagierende Steinzeitmensch bricht sich Bahn, was in der körperlichen Gewalt, die der Wissenschaftler gegen den Hausbesitzer anwendet, und im Niederbrennen von dessen Haus kulminiert.

In den Traditionszusammenhang des »mad scientist«-Topos gehört auch, daß die Genialität des Wissenschaftlers mit übernatürlichen Kräften in Verbindung gebracht wird. In den frühen »mad scientist«-Darstellungen zeigt der Forscher nicht selten Züge des Alchimisten, Astrologen oder Zauberers. Das Bild des mit dem Teufel im Bund stehenden faustischen Wissenschaftlers wirkt bis in das 20. Jahrhundert nach. Auch in Wells' Roman zeigen sich Anklänge daran: Als Kemp zum ersten Mal mit der Unsichtbarkeit seines unheimlichen Besuchers konfrontiert wird, spricht er die ungläubig-abergläubischen Worte: »But what devilry must happen to make a man invisible?« (Kap. 17). Freilich ist dem naturwissenschaftlich gebildeten H. G. Wells daran gelegen, Griffins Zustand nicht als Ergebnis schierer Teufelei und bloßen Zauberspuks erscheinen zu lassen. Der langatmige pseudowissenschaftliche Diskurs Griffins soll im Leser jene »willing suspension of disbelief«[9] auslösen, die ihm die Geschichte als halbwegs plausibel erscheinen läßt. Man hat Wells vorgeworfen, er habe durch das Aufstellen fragwürdiger wissenschaftlicher Prämissen in *The Invisible Man* gegen die Maxime Coleridges verstoßen.[10] Diese Kritik greift zu kurz, da im Grunde fast jede Science Fiction – seien ihre Ausgangsprämissen wissenschaftlich noch so stimmig – mehr oder weniger pseudowissenschaftlich verfährt. Denn ihre Zukunftsvisionen, Alternativentwürfe und Extrapolationen sind zwangsläufig spekulativ, d.h. stellen mehr oder weniger wahrscheinliche Mutmaßungen dar.

H. G. Wells und die Tradition der Romanze

Es wäre zweifellos falsch, anzunehmen, H. G. Wells würde in allen Details wissenschaftliche Stimmigkeit erreichen wollen. Auf physikalische und technische Detailrichtigkeit kommt es dem einer mechanistischen Weltanschauung abholden Schriftsteller nicht an. In diesem Sinne ist er pseudowissenschaftlich, und er steht in seiner Erzählung vom Unsichtbaren dem Sagenmotiv der Tarnkappe tatsächlich näher als den physikalischen Gesetzen der Optik. Somit stellt sich die Unsichtbarkeit ungeachtet ihrer wissenschaftlichen Erklärung tatsächlich als das Ergebnis jenes Zauberkunststücks heraus, das die Dorfbe-

9 Diesen Ausdruck prägte Samuel Taylor Coleridge in Kapitel 14 seiner *Biographia Literaria* von 1817.
10 Vgl. Suvin, *Poetik der Science Fiction*, S. 272.

wohner in Kapitel 7 hinter dem Phänomen wittern.[11] Wells macht aus dem Erfinden objektiver Unwahrheiten keinen Hehl. Er, der seine Geschichten »exercises in imagination« nennt, bekennt sich zu der Tradition des phantasievollen Fabulierens und der unglaublichen Geschichte. Die Bezeichnung »romances« für seine frühen Erzählwerke weisen ihn als Fortführer der Romanzentradition, als Vertreter und Erneuerer einer Erzählgattung aus, in der abenteuerliche, unerhörte, phantastische und wunderbare Ereignisse geschildert werden. Wenn Griffin seine Erlebnisse als »my adventure« (Kap. 21) bezeichnet, sieht er sich nicht nur als Wissenschaftler, sondern auch als Abenteurer, der die unglaublichsten und bizarrsten Dinge erlebt. Das Attribut »scientific«, das Wells der Bezeichnung »romance« an die Seite stellt, verweist auf das wissenschaftliche Element, das die Fiktion als glaubwürdig erscheinen läßt, wobei – wie J. Hienger zu Recht sagt[12] – die plausible Erklärung zur unabhängigen Erfindung hinzutritt, nicht jedoch ihre Ursache darstellt. Wells hat sich durch das Anknüpfen an die Romanzentradition ein Potential an Möglichkeiten phantastischen Fabulierens eröffnet, das er andererseits durch das Mittel der (pseudo)wissenschaftlich-rationalen Erklärung bändigt und domestiziert. Geschickt die formale Struktur der Romanze (Spannung, Abwechslungsreichtum der Ereignisse, einfache Handlungselemente) aufgreifend, schafft er sich ein Vehikel für den Transport einer Idee, einer Aussage und eines Sinngehalts, deren Anlaß die wissenschaftliche Idee – das Novum – ist.[13]

H. G. Wells hat – wie mehrfach gezeigt – zahlreiche Anleihen an die Gothic novel gemacht, auf deren Topoi, Situationen, Handlungsmuster, Requisiten und Schauereffekte er zurückgreift. Auch dies ist im Rahmen der Rezeption der Romanzentradition zu sehen, da der Schauerroman nichts anderes als

11 Vgl. ebd., S. 266, 288.
12 Vgl. Jörg Hienger, *Literarische Zukunftsphantastik. Eine Studie über Science Fiction,* Göttingen 1972, S. 18.
13 Zur Romanzentradition Wells' siehe Ulrich Suerbaum / Ulrich Broich / Raimund Borgmeier, *Science Fiction. Theorie und Geschichte, Themen und Typen, Form und Weltbild,* Stuttgart 1981, S. 45–50.

eine aus dem Geist des 18. Jahrhunderts entstandene Form der Romanze ist. Seine »scientific romances« ordnet der englische Schriftsteller in die gleiche literarische Klasse ein wie Mary Shelleys prometheischen Schauerroman *Frankenstein*, der den direkten Weg zur modernen Science Fiction weist. In diesem Roman mag Wells Anregungen zu manchem an die Gothic novel erinnernden Schauerrequisit, vor allem aber zu der sinistren Gestalt des »mad scientist« gefunden haben, die in Griffin (oder Dr. Moreau) wiedersteht und zu einer schrecklichen Verschmelzung von Wissenschaftler und Monster mutiert.

Die Jagd auf den Unsichtbaren

Die Flucht nach Iping erfolgt aus der nüchternen Erkenntnis Griffins, daß die Unsichtbarkeit ein Fluch ist, der ihn zu »a wrapped-up mystery, a swathed and bandaged caricature of a man!« (Kap. 23) hat werden lassen. Sowohl in physischer als auch in moralisch-ethischer Hinsicht erlebt und erleidet er das Pariah-Dasein des in den Kategorien des geordneten menschlichen und gesellschaftlichen Zusammenlebens nicht mehr faßbaren Ausgestoßenen, dessen Exilierung er sich indessen selbst zuzuschreiben hat. Paradoxerweise hat Griffin nach seinen frustrierenden Erlebnissen die Idee von der Unsichtbarkeit als Mittel absoluter Macht immer noch nicht aufgegeben, dies nicht zuletzt auch eine Reaktion auf das ratlose und plumpe Verhalten der Menschen angesichts seines Zustandes. So schwankt er zwischen dem Wunsch, wieder sichtbar zu werden (Kap. 23), und der wahrhaft wahnsinnigen Perspektive, mittels der Unsichtbarkeit Tod und Terror über die Menschen zu bringen, um sie zu beherrschen: »And that Invisible Man [...] must now establish a Reign of Terror« (Kap. 24). Griffins Versuch, Kemp als Komplizen seiner wahnhaften und mörderischen Machtvision zu gewinnen, mißlingt, da dieser aus den Worten des Unsichtbaren dessen mörderische Gefährlichkeit, brutalen Egoismus, rücksichtslose Eigennützigkeit und Wahnsinn erkennt. Er weiß, daß diese Eigenschaften Griffin außerhalb der menschlichen Gemeinschaft stellen (»He has cut himself off from his kind«, Kap. 25). In diesem Sinn bezeichnet Kemp, der schon früh die mörderischen Instinkte des Unsichtbaren erkannte (»[…] he's mad! Homicidal!«, Kap. 18), diesen als »inhuman« (Kap. 25). Aus dem Gefühl der ethischen und sozialen Verantwortung heraus verrät daher der Arzt und Wissenschaftler seinen grotesken Besucher an die Polizei und teilt ihr dessen Versteck mit (Kap. 18 und 24).

Erneut flüchtet Griffin, in wilder Entschlossenheit, seine Haut zu retten. Damit wird strukturell die Schlußphase des Romans eingeleitet. Es beginnt die Hetzjagd auf den Unsichtbaren, die mit dessen Tod endet.

Die Worte, mit denen Kemp die Gefährlichkeit Griffins Colonel Adye, dem Polizeichef von Burdock, schildert, spiegeln die hektische Diktion einer Katastrophenankündigung wider, wie man sie von dem Invasionsroman The War of the Worlds her kennt. Hat bereits in Kapitel 15 der Ruf »The Invisible Man is coming« den Ort Burdock in Panik und Schrecken versetzt und eine Stimmung der Heimsuchung durch das Fremde, Unerklärliche und Böse erzeugt – anders wäre die Stimmung kaum ausgefallen, hätte es sich um eine Invasion vom Mars gehandelt –, so beschwört die Bezeichnung Griffins nicht nur als Gefahr, sondern als Unheil (»disaster«, Kap. 25), das über die Bewohner des Dorfes hereinbricht, eine an die disaster novel gemahnende Situation. Schließlich läßt die gefährliche Gewalt, die Griffin über den Ort bringt, die Ereignisse in Iping geradezu als harmlos erscheinen. Der sich konstituierende Kriegsrat (»council of war«) ist ein weiteres Handlungselement, das sich in zahlreichen Invasions- und Katastrophengeschichten des literarischen und filmischen Bereichs der Science Fiction findet. Die Flucht des Unsichtbaren ist gekennzeichnet von dessen Gewalt, Raserei und verzweifelter Wut über Kemps Verrat, für die der namenlose Erzähler sogar so etwas wie Verständnis aufbringen kann (»we may […] even sympathise a little«, Kap. 26). Während sich der Kreis um den Gehetzten immer enger zieht, ereignet sich der Mord an Mr. Wicksteed, dessen Umstände der Leser den Beobachtungen und Vermutungen des Erzählers entnimmt. Eines scheint klar: So grausam die Umstände des

Mordes sind – dem Opfer wird mit einem eisernen Pfahl der Schädel eingeschlagen –, das Verbrechen ist nicht das Ergebnis blindwütigen Rasens seitens des Unsichtbaren, sondern eher das Resultat tragischer Verkettung. Immerhin bewahrheitet sich die Drohung, die Griffin in Kapitel 23 gegen jene »idiots« und »silly creatures« ausstößt, die sich ihm aus Tolpatschigkeit in den Weg stellen: »If I have much more of it, I shall go wild, – I shall start mowing 'em.« Sehr wohl das Ergebnis monomanischer Rache und des erklärten Willens, Terror zu erzeugen, ist andererseits die Absicht Griffins, sich Kemp vorzunehmen und seine Herrschaft über den Ort Burdock zu etablieren. In megalomaner Selbstüberschätzung schreibt er dem Arzt: »This is day one of year one of the new epoch, – the Epoch of the Invisible Man. I am Invisible Man the First« (Kap. 27). War der Mord an Wicksteed eher das Ergebnis eines Zufalls, wird jetzt Mord als Instrument zur Durchsetzung von Rache und Terror kaltblütig geplant.

Die Belagerung von Kemps Haus durch den Unsichtbaren schildert Wells im Stile des Thrillers, wobei er die aus zahlreichen Kriminalerzählungen und Agentengeschichten bzw. -filmen bekannte Situation – ein Verfolgter verbarrikadiert sich in seinem Haus oder seiner Wohnung, ein schurkischer Verfolger versucht sich gewaltsam Zutritt zu verschaffen – spannend und geschickt in Szene setzt. Durch die Unsichtbarkeit des Verfolgers werden nicht nur die Spannung erhöht und der Nervenkitzel verstärkt (man beachte die Geräusche im Haus, die Nervosität Kemps usw.), sondern die Situation grotesk verfremdet. Der Revolver – Standardrequisit eines jeden Krimis und Agententhrillers – schwebt, nachdem er den Besitzer gewechselt hat, in der Luft, ehe er dem Polizeichef zum Schicksal wird, von unsichtbarer Hand geworfene Steine zerschlagen Fensterscheiben, eine von Geisterhand geführte Axt zerhackt die Fensterläden und trifft einen Polizisten am Kopf.

Die Belagerung des Hauses durch den Unsichtbaren einschließlich der danach stattfindenden, mit vertauschten Rollen ablaufenden Verfolgungsjagd – Griffin wird zum Jäger, Kemp zum Gejagten – erwächst aus einer psychologischen Motivation Griffins, die ihre Ursache im persönlichen Verhältnis hat, das

dieser zu anderen Menschen aufbaut. Entstanden seine bishe-
rigen Erlebnisse, Erfahrungen und Vergehen in London, Iping
und Burdock (Gewalttätigkeiten, Einbrüche, Brandstiftung
usw.) aus der Unerträglichkeit seiner Conditio mit einer ver-
ständnislosen Umwelt, ohne daß eine persönliche Beziehung
zu einem anderen Menschen involviert ist, so entsteht durch
das Zusammentreffen mit Kemp ein persönlicher Konnex, der
sich auf frühere Bekanntschaft und die Hoffnung gründet, dieser könne dem Unsichtbaren helfen, sei es, um wieder sichtbar
zu werden, oder, um sein Schreckensregime zu etablieren. Die
Ebene persönlicher Beziehungen hat sich bei Griffin bislang ex
negativo definiert. Während seiner Studien macht er negative
Erfahrungen mit Oliver, seinem Professor, der sich neugierig in
seine Entdeckung hineinzudrängen versucht (Kap. 19), die Stu-
denten, die er unterrichtet, verhöhnt er als Narren, den Vater
bestiehlt er skrupellos. Einmal klingt die Beziehung zu einer
Frau an (Kap. 20), die er in der High Street sieht – eine Freun-
din seit zehn Jahren, deren Spur sich jedoch verliert. Unfähig zu
persönlichen Beziehungen schon zu Zeiten seiner Normalität,
schleppt Griffin dieses emotionale Defizit auch in der Unsichtbarkeit mit sich herum, wo es sich noch verschlimmert. Um
so gravierender ist es daher, wenn der Unsichtbare erleben
muß, daß sein Versuch der Kontaktaufnahme durch Verrat zer-
stört wird. Enttäuschung und Rache sind Reaktionen, die sowohl von psychologischer als auch von handlungskonstitutiver
Relevanz sind. Die psychologische, sprich kriminelle Energie,
die Griffin aktiviert, entlädt sich direkt auf der Handlungs-
ebene: Es kommt zu der zerstörerischen Belagerung des
Hauses, zum Mord am Polizeichef und zu der rücksichtslosen
Verfolgung Kemps bis ins Dorf, wo das Schicksal den Unsichtbaren ereilt.

Der Tod des Unsichtbaren

Der Rollentausch vom Gejagten zum Jäger führt Griffin direkt
in den Untergang. Die zerstörerische Energie gerät zur Selbst-
zerstörung. Ein mit Spaten und Stöcken bewaffneter oder sich

auf die Kraft seiner Fäuste verlassender Mob stürzt sich auf den Unsichtbaren, um ihn zu vernichten. Aus der verschreckten Dorfbevölkerung ist ein entfesselter Pöbel geworden.[14] Dies ist die Folge von Griffins skrupellosem Terrorismus, ist letzten Endes sein eigenes Werk.

Man hat die Schlußszene des Buches, die Vernichtung des Unsichtbaren, als eine Art Exorzismus interpretiert, den die Gesellschaft an diesem vornimmt. Sie stempelt Griffin zum Sündenbock für die gefährliche Anmaßung der Wissenschaft und stößt ihn aus ihren Reihen aus.[15] Diese Interpretation, so richtig sie auch sein mag, reicht jedoch nicht aus. Was die Szene vor allem enthüllt, ist das starke affektive Moment, das sich mit der Tötung Griffins einstellt. Im Augenblick des Todes wird der Unsichtbare sichtbar. Jedoch erregt die Sichtbarwerdung des erschlagenen Fremden und seines geschundenen Körpers beim Leser kein Gefühl des Triumphes, sondern eher Mitleid. Wesentlich stärker noch als an anderen Stellen des Buches (z. B. beim Umherirren in London; vgl. Griffins Bericht) läßt Wells den Leser dem Unsichtbaren gegenüber Mitgefühl empfinden. Die sichtbar gewordene Qual Griffins läßt diesen nicht mehr erschreckend, sondern nur noch mitleidenswert erscheinen. Es zeigt sich augenfällig der auf die Hybris eines brillanten Wissenschaftlers folgende Fall, der in einer physischen Vernichtung, die kläglich und erbärmlich ist, vonstatten geht.

Die Empfindung des Mitgefühls, die sich beim Leser einstellt, ist nicht zuletzt das Ergebnis der superben Beschreibung physischer Details, die der biologisch gebildete Autor bei der Sichtbarwerdung des toten Griffin verwendet. Wird durch die Sichtbarkeit in gewisser Weise auch eine Rückkehr in die mensch-

---

14 Nicht zustimmen kann man angesichts des entfesselten Mobs der Auffassung von Norman und Jeanne Mackenzie, die argumentieren, Wells habe Griffin als Symbol für die Bestie im Menschen gesetzt, während er die Bürger als Vertreter von Ordnung, Vernunft und Tradition darstelle; vgl. Norman Mackenzie / Jeanne Mackenzie, *The Time Traveller*, London 1973, S. 126 f.

15 Vgl. B. Bergonzi, *The Early H. G. Wells*, S. 120.

liche Gemeinschaft ausgedrückt, so bleibt der Anblick Griffins
– das weiße Haar, die weiße Haut, die roten Augen – dennoch
fremd, anders, ja fast monströs und bildet einen scharfen Kontrast zu der idyllisch-dörflichen Umgebung,[16] die durch das
Auftauchen des Fremden vorübergehend aus dem Lot geraten
ist.

Kemp und Griffin: zwei konträre Wissenschaftlertypen

Schon rein äußerlich unterscheiden sich Kemp und Griffin
deutlich voneinander. Beide sind jung, doch während jener als
schlank, blond und groß geschildert wird, ist dieser von kräfti-
ger Statur, verfügt über erhebliche Körperkräfte, die er ziel-
genau einzusetzen weiß, und hat die weiße Haut- und Haar-
farbe des Albinos. Brillant als Wissenschaftler und Forscher,
findet er in seiner Lehrtätigkeit in einem kleinen Provinz-Col-
lege keine Anerkennung. Fasziniert von den Gesetzen des
Lichts und der Optik, entwickelt er eine Passion für das Experimentieren und eine Hingabe für wissenschaftliches Forschen. Allmählich steigert er sich in eine Manie hinein, und er
scheut kein Mittel, um sein Ziel – die Unsichtbarkeit – zu erreichen. In seiner Skrupellosigkeit kennt er weder Hemmun-
gen noch Reue. Dennoch zeigen sich Ansätze von Schuldge-
fühl, was seine um das Begräbnis des Vaters kreisenden Gedanken und Alpträume (siehe z. B. Kap. 20 und 22) beweisen.
Unter dem Einfluß von Stimulanzien verstärkt sich Griffins
von Natur aus angelegte Disposition zum Cholerischen. Hef-
tige Wutanfälle und mörderische Anwandlungen sind die
Folge. Die Entfremdung von der Gesellschaft wird total, die
Menschen wenden sich gegen ihn, den sie fürchten, und vernichten ihn. Griffins Ende ist tragisch, es ist der Tiefpunkt einer tragischen Entwicklung, die damit begann, daß er sich Zutritt zu den verbotenen Geheimnissen und Schrecken der Unsichtbarkeit verschaffte. Das tragische Ende als Strafe für sich
verabsolutierendes und verbotenes wissenschaftliches Streben

16 Siehe Robert Scholes / Eric S. Rabkin, *Science Fiction. History –
Science – Vision,* London / Oxford / New York 1977, S. 23 f.

stigmatisiert Griffin als faustischen Wissenschaftler, als mit
den Mächten des Bösen paktierender Alchimist, als Forscher
vom Schlage eines Dr. Frankenstein und Dr. Jekyll. Seine
Bestrafung bedeutet die Absage an die Anmaßungen einer
zügellosen Wissenschaft.
In krassem Gegensatz zu Griffin steht Dr. Kemp. Er, der die
gleiche Universität besucht hat wie jener, personifiziert den Typ
des »normalen«, geradlinigen, nüchternen, korrekten und hu-
manen Wissenschaftlers. Auch er ist ehrgeizig und neugierig.
Als Alter ego H. G. Wells' (man vergleiche dessen wissenschaftliche Laufbahn) hofft er auf eine Mitgliedschaft in der
Royal Society. Im Gegensatz zu Griffin läßt Kemp es nicht zu,
daß wissenschaftliche Forschung die ethischen Parameter der
menschlichen Gesellschaft überschreitet. Nicht über das erfin-
derische Genie des Unsichtbaren verfügend, ist soziale Verantwortung für ihn ein Imperativ. Wenn seine Gedanken – ähnlich
denen des Zeitreisenden in *The Time Machine* – um die Zeitdi-
mension kreisen und in die ferne Zukunft schweifen, dann in-
teressieren ihn an letzterer die sozialen Bedingungen (Kap. 17).
Der ethische Pragmatiker Kemp,[17] jeglicher Gewalt und Brutalität abhold, erkennt rasch die Gefährlichkeit von Griffins
sprunghafter und manischer Wesensart. Er ermahnt diesen,
nicht gegen die menschliche Rasse zu handeln, seine einzelgän-
gerische Isolation aufzugeben und den Menschen zu vertrauen.
Vor allem fordert er ihn auf, seine wissenschaftlichen Erkennt-
nisse bekannt zu machen und mit anderen zu teilen (Kap. 24).
In dieser Aufforderung kristallisiert sich wohl der deutlichste
Unterschied zwischen den beiden Wissenschaftlern heraus.
Wissenschaftliche Erkenntnis darf nach Kemp nicht der Besitz
eines einzelnen zur Durchsetzung egoistischer und letztlich ver-
brecherischer Ziele sein, sondern muß zum Wohl aller dem
Nutzen der Öffentlichkeit zugeführt werden. Aus dieser ethischen Grundsatzüberlegung heraus vollzieht Kemp schließlich
den Verrat an seinem Antagonisten. Seine aus der Sorge um
das Allgemeinwohl resultierende Handlungsweise hat natür-

17 Vgl. Bergonzi, *The Early H. G. Wells*, S. 117.

lich auch einen negativen Beigeschmack, verrät Kemp doch einen Menschen, der ihm Vertrauen schenkt und Hilfe von ihm erwartet. Wells erlaubt es daher dem Leser, Verständnis für Griffin zu haben, wenn dieser bittere Rache an dem Arzt nehmen will. Dieser muß denn auch Lehrgeld zahlen und selbst die Ängste eines Gejagten erleiden, für den die Türen der Häuser verschlossen sind (Kap. 28).[18]

Wertung, Kritik, Aussage von »The Invisible Man«

Die Kritik ist sich einig darüber, daß *The Invisible Man* über Klarheit in Konzeption und Aufbau, sorgfältige Komposition, homogene Struktur, gedankliche Originalität sowie Ideenreichtum verfügt und in einem erfrischenden, anschaulichen und gut lesbaren Stil verfaßt ist.[19] B. Bergonzi allerdings kritisiert die abrupten Stimmungsübergänge, die »superficial variety of moods«[20], und sieht in dem langatmigen analytischen Bericht Griffins »a somewhat clumsy device«.[21]
Ob diese Einschätzung zutrifft, sei dahingestellt, ist doch der rückblendende Bericht in der narrativen und dramatischen Literatur ein überaus häufig anzutreffendes und auch erfolgreich angewandtes Strukturmittel, dessen Länge in diesem Roman durchaus nicht zu struktureller Unausgewogenheit führt.
Es ist unverkennbar, daß der von Joseph Conrad als »uncommonly fine« gepriesene Roman – wie auch die anderen frühen Romanzen des »pessimistischen Zukunftsträumers«[22] H. G. Wells – starke Züge einer Parabel aufweist. Faßt man die wesentlichen Elemente, die eine Parabel konstituieren, ins Auge – eine einfache Geschichte, die eine Moral auf implizitem Wege

---

18 Zu den konträren Wissenschaftlertypen siehe Rendall H. Keenan, *The Major Works of H. G. Wells,* New York 1970 (Monarch Notes), S. 67 f.
19 Vgl. etwa Albert Baugh, *A Literary History of England,* London 1948, S. 1559; Bergonzi, S. 113, 121; Norman und Jeanne Mackenzie, S. 116.
20 Bergonzi, S. 121.
21 Ebd., S. 113.
22 J. Hienger, *Literarische Zukunftsphantastik,* S. 21.

lehrt und eine symbolische Bedeutung trägt, die eine sittliche
Wahrheit lehrt, die sich an Aufzuklärende wendet, um sie im
Besonderen das Allgemeine, im scheinbar Fremden das Eigene
erkennen zu lassen und für sittliche Ordnung zu werben[23] –,
dann fällt auf, daß in *The Invisible Man* ungewöhnliche, unerklärliche Ereignisse dargestellt werden, die über ihr konkretes
Eigenleben hinaus eine zweite, eigentliche Aussage vermitteln,
deren signalhafte Bedeutungsträger sie sind.[24] H. G. Wells dra-
matisiert im Rahmen phantastischer Ereignisse Wahrheiten
über die menschliche Natur und die Conditio humana und ver-
bindet damit eine Moral. Diese Moral definiert sich für den en-
gagierten Sozialisten Wells im Sinne einer sozialen Botschaft.
Was innerhalb der menschlichen Gemeinschaft vor sich geht,
darf nicht von der Verantwortung für eben diese Gemeinschaft
losgelöst werden. Griffins wissenschaftlicher Wahn, sein
Machtstreben und seine moralische Prinzipienlosigkeit vermitteln das Bild einer Wissenschaft, die in dem Sinne pervertiert
ist, als sie sich ihrer sozialen Verantwortung völlig entzogen hat.
Kemps Appell an Griffin, seine wissenschaftliche Entdeckung
mit der Gemeinschaft zu teilen, anstatt sie zu egoistischen, ge-
meingefährlichen Zwecken zu mißbrauchen, entspringt dem
ethischen Gewissen einer sich gesellschaftlich verpflichtet ver-
stehenden Wissenschaft. Griffin, der die Anmaßungen einer
menschenverachtenden, »a-sozialen« Wissenschaft verkörpert,
muß im Kontext der menschlichen Gemeinschaft scheitern.
Sein Hochmut kommt vor dem Fall. Als eine Geschichte von
der Hybris und deren unvermeidlichem Scheitern ist *The Invisible Man* eine moralische Geschichte, eine Parabel. H. G.
Wells – selbst naturwissenschaftlich (aus)gebildet – drückt in
seiner Romanze seine Ambivalenz[25] gegenüber der Wissenschaft aus, die er einerseits bewundernswert findet, wenn sie

23 Siehe dazu Gero von Wilpert, *Sachwörterbuch der Literatur,* Stuttgart 1964, S. 490f., und Otto F. Best, *Handbuch literarischer Fachbe-
griffe,* Frankfurt a. M. 1979, S. 190f.
24 Vgl. Rein A. Zondergeld, *Lexikon der phantastischen Literatur,*
Frankfurt a. M. 1983, S. 288.
25 Vgl. N. und J. Mackenzie, *The Time Traveller,* S. 126.

die Bestie im Menschen zu bändigen vermag, die er aber andererseits ablehnt, wenn sie Forscher wie Griffin hervorbringt,
die außer Kontrolle geraten sind und deren egomanisches Genie zu keinem menschlichen Mitgefühl fähig ist. Was Wells in
The Invisible Man darstellen wollte, waren nach seinen eigenen
Worten »the dangers of power without control, the develop-
ment of the intelligence at the expense of human sympathy«.[26]
Das Menschliche und die Verantwortung für das Gemeinwesen
sind die Anliegen, die der englische Schriftsteller in das Zen-
trum seiner sozialkritisch gefärbten Romanze stellt. Wells gibt
sich als Vertreter engagierter und ernsthafter Science Fiction
insofern zu erkennen, als für ihn nicht die Erfindung der Unsichtbarkeit als wissenschaftliches Phänomen per se im Mittel-
punkt steht, sondern dessen Auswirkungen auf den Unsichtbaren und sein Verhältnis zu der ihn umgebenden, aber auch
ausgrenzenden Gesellschaft.[27] Wenn der namenlose Erzähler
im Epilog das Experiment Griffins nicht nur als »strange«, sondern zugleich als »evil« bezeichnet, so zeigt sich darin erneut
die moralische Verurteilung einer für die Gesellschaft und die
Menschen unheilvollen Wissenschaft.

Das Verkünden einer sozialen Moral weist H. G. Wells als Vertreter des ästhetischen Prinzips des »Prodesse« aus, das Ein-
binden dieser Moral in eine spannende, anschauliche, an
Schauer- und komischen Effekten reiche Handlung als Verfechter des »Delectare«. Es sei zum Abschluß der enthusiasti-
sche Kommentar Joseph Conrads wiedergegeben, den dieser
nach der Lektüre von *The Invisible Man* seinem Kollegen zu-
sandte:

> »I am always powerfully impressed by your work. Impressed
> is *the* word, O Realist of the Fantastic! [...] if you want to
> know what impresses me it is to see how you contrive to give

---

26 Zit. nach: Geoffrey West, *H. G. Wells: A Sketch for a Portrait,* London 1930, S. 112.
27 Zu diesem Kriterium der Science Fiction siehe Isaac Asimov, »Plä-
doyer für Science-fiction«, in: *Der Spiegel,* 26 (6. März 1972), Nr. 11,
S. 138 f.

over humanity to the clutches of the Impossible and yet manage
to keep it down (or up) to its humanity, to its flesh, blood, sor-
row, folly. *That* is the achievement.«[28]

H. G. Wells und der Film: die Verfilmung von »The Invisible Man«

Es ist im allgemeinen wohl bekannt, wird aber in den
H. G. Wells gewidmeten Monographien, Gesamtdarstellungen
und Biographien entweder nur beiläufig oder überhaupt nicht
erwähnt, daß die Werke des englischen Schriftstellers schon
früh eine starke Anziehungskraft auf Filmregisseure und -pro-
duzenten ausübten und in ihnen den Wunsch weckten, diese zu
verfilmen. Die überwiegende Zahl der Verfilmungen Wells-
scher Bücher basiert auf Stoffen, die dem Bereich der Science
Fiction angehören. Dies hat wohl seine Ursache darin, daß zum
einen Themen wie Mondflug, die Erfindungen von »mad scientists«, Kriege in der Zukunft, utopische und dystopische Ge-
sellschaftsvisionen, Zeitreise, Invasion vom Mars oder Riesen-
wuchs von Tieren und Menschen zum Standardrepertoire des
Science-Fiction- und z. T. Horrorfilms gehören und zum anderen, daß H. G. Wells dazu die wohl interessantesten und kom-
petentesten Vorlagen geliefert hat.
Es ist eine weniger bekannte Tatsache, daß Wells bei den Verfilmungen seiner Werke selbst eine aktive Rolle spielte, war
dieser doch ein ausgesprochener Filmfan. Bereits 1895 plante
er mit dem britischen Filmpionier Robert William Paul eine
Realisierung von *The Time Machine.* Dem Projekt war jedoch
kein Erfolg beschieden. 1902 entstand George Méliès' *Reise
zum Mond,* ein Film, an dessen Realisierung Wells zwar nicht
persönlich beteiligt war, der jedoch von ihm inspiriert wurde. In
den dreißiger Jahren entstanden eine Reihe von Filmen, bei deren Realisierung Wells z. T. aktiv mitwirkte. So schrieb er für
die Verfilmung seines Romans *The Shape of Things to Come*
(1933) das Drehbuch (Titel des Films: *Things to Come,* 1936;

28 Zit. nach: N. und J. Mackenzie, S. 141.

Regie: William Cameron Menzies, Produzent: der englische
Filmzar Alexander Korda). Auch bei der im gleichen Jahr ent-
standenen filmischen Adaptation von *The Man Who Could
Work Miracles* (Produzent war wiederum Alexander Korda)
wirkte der Autor aktiv mit. Bereits 1932 waren *The Island of
Lost Souls* (Regie: Erle C. Kenton; mit Charles Laughton als
Hauptdarsteller) nach dem Roman *The Island of Dr. Moreau*
(1896) und 1933 *The Invisible Man* (Regie: James Whale) entstanden.

Der Film nahm H. G. Wells so sehr gefangen, daß er zeitweise
sogar daran dachte, ganz in das Filmgeschäft einzusteigen. 1935
begab er sich nach Hollywood und führte Gespräche mit Char-
lie Chaplin und Cecil B. de Mille. Der Aufenthalt in Amerika
brachte jedoch nicht den gewünschten Erfolg.

Nach dem Zweiten Weltkrieg entstanden weitere, hauptsäch-
lich amerikanische Verfilmungen der Romane Wells': 1953 *The
War of the Worlds* (USA, Regie: Byron Haskin), 1960 *The Time
Machine* (USA, Regie: George Pal), 1964 *The First Men on the
Moon* (GB, Regie: Nathan Juran), 1976 *Food of the Gods*
(USA, Regie: Bert J. Gordon), 1977 das enttäuschende Re-
make von *Island of Lost Souls* unter dem gleichen Titel wie das
Buch (USA, Regie: Don Taylor; mit Burt Lancaster in der
Rolle des Dr. Moreau).

Die Verfilmung von *The Invisible Man* stellte insofern eine besondere Herausforderung an Filmemacher dar, als einmal das
Thema der Unsichtbarkeit einschließlich der Schreckensge-
stalt des »mad scientist« einen probaten Stoff für einen Horrorfilm mit SF-Elementen hergab und zum anderen die Darstellung des Phänomens der Unsichtbarkeit besonders reizvoll
für einen Trickfilmspezialisten sein mußte. So war es kein Zu-
fall, daß die auf Horror spezialisierte Filmgesellschaft Universal und der britische Horrorfilmregisseur James Whale (er
hatte die beiden Frankensteinfilme inszeniert) sich mit dem
amerikanischen Trickfilmspezialisten John P. Fulton (1902 bis
1966) zusammentaten, der über ein für die damalige Zeit
erstaunliches Tricktechnikrepertoire verfügte. Es herrschte
damals in den Hollywood-Studios die Meinung vor, daß die

filmische Realisierung der Wellsschen Romanze unmöglich
sei.

Lassen wir noch einmal einige Szenen aus dem Buch Revue
passieren, in denen die Unsichtbarkeit Griffins sinnfällig dargestellt wird: der Unsichtbare in seiner Vermummung ohne
Kopf und Hände (Kap. 3 und 7), der Besuch Griffins bei Kemp
(Kap. 17) mit der Schilderung des in der Luft schwebenden
blutbefleckten Verbands, der unsichtbaren Hand, die Kemp ergreift und fesselt, des in der Luft hängenden Whiskeyglases, der
Bewegung des Stuhls, des eingedrückten Sitzkissens, des essen-
den und eine Zigarre rauchenden Unsichtbaren, die unsichtbare Katze mit ihren leuchtenden Augen und die Unsichtbarwerdung Griffins (Kap. 20), der in der Luft schwebende Revolver (Kap. 27) oder schließlich die Sichtbarwerdung des toten
Griffin (Kap. 28). An diesen Szenen läßt sich ersehen, wie
schwierig, ja unmöglich die filmische Umsetzung des Romans
erscheinen mußte. Wenn sie dennoch gelang, dann wegen des
Geschicks des besonders auf Elemente des Makabren und
schwarzen Humors setzenden Regisseurs und des Könnens des
Trickexperten Fulton. Dessen Spezialeffekte – z. B. agierte ein
Stuntman mit schwarzer Maske und schwarzen Handschuhen
vor einem schwarzen Hintergrund oder es kann die *wire*-Tech-
nik zur Anwendung – wurden auch in den meisten Fort-
setzungsfilmen um die Figur des Unsichtbaren angewandt.
1939 entstand *The Invisible Man Returns* (Regie: Joe May,
Drehbuch: Curt Siodmak), 1942 *Invisible Agent* (Regie:
Frank Lloyd), 1944 *The Invisible Man's Revenge* (Regie: Ford
Beebe), 1951 *Abbot and Costello Meet the Invisible Man*
(Regie: Charles Lamont). In diesen Fortsetzungen verlagert
sich der Schwerpunkt vom Science-Fiction- / Horrorfilm zum
Suspense- bzw. Agententhriller (Elemente davon sind – wie zu
sehen war – im Roman vorhanden) und schließlich zur parodi-
stischen Klamotte. Von der erfolgreichen filmischen Adaptation aus dem Jahre 1933 waren diese Werke natürlich weit entfernt.

Unter den zahlreichen Verfilmungen und Fortsetzungen des
Themas der Unsichtbarkeit (allein über dreißig Filme sind ihm

gewidmet) befinden sich auch eine britische (1958) und amerikanische (1975) Fernsehserie, die sich, bedingt durch ihren seriellen Charakter, ebenfalls weit von dem Wellsschen Original entfernen.[29]

Klaus Werner

---

29 Zur Verfilmung der Wellsschen Romane siehe Brian Aldiss, *Der Millionen-Jahre-Traum. Die Geschichte der Science Fiction*, Bergisch Gladbach 1980, S. 179f.; Rolf Gießen, *Lexikon des phantastischen Films*, Bd. 1, Frankfurt a.M. / Berlin / Wien 1984, S. 245, und Bd. 2, S. 210, 334; N. und J. Mackenzie, S. 389–392; P. Nicholls (Hrsg.), *The Encyclopedia of Science Fiction*, S. 313; G. Seeßlen, *Kino des Utopischen*, S. 120–123.

Inhalt

The Invisible Man

Fremdsprachentexte

IN RECLAMS UNIVERSAL-BIBLIOTHEK

Englische Prosa und Gedichte

Philipp Reclam jun. Stuttgart